things these first satelli [barcode] the facts that may be ◁ S0-BKG-477 the moon, the near planets, and the sun; the possibility of predicting future weather accurately (thereby revolutionizing farming); the knowledge that may be gained about atmosphere: new information about the mysterious cosmic rays and how they affect our lives.

Mr. Bergaust and Mr. Beller also give the background of the present rocket and satellite program, from an explanation of rocket motors and launching programs to the difficulties of getting even a small object into an orbit. And they present an exciting account of how the basic knowledge of the world and the universe may be changed and broadened by the new information collected by the tiny circling satellites.

The authors explain how the satellite program may answer many of the old questions concerning life on Mars and Venus and what is on the other side of the moon. And they feel that the project will force the asking of new questions. Man will be exposed to a frontier he has never before been able to penetrate — and man has always looked to the sky and wondered what lay beyond.

Printed in the U.S.A.

BOUT THE AUTHORS...

Erik Bergaust is rocket and missile editor of *American Aviation* and guided-missile consultant for several engineering and aircraft companies. Born and educated in Norway, Mr. Bergaust is a naturalized United States citizen. He has worked in this country as a project engineer in rocket-propellant research. Internationally respected as an aviation writer, he has written numerous newspaper and magazine articles and several aviation books.

William Beller, managing editor of *Aero Digest,* holds aeronautical engineering degrees from Georgia Tech and N.Y.U., where he was a De la Cierva Fellow. An expert in aerodynamics and aeronautical design, he has been a faculty member of the University of Southern California and the Polytechnic Institute of Brooklyn. He has also worked for Hughes Aircraft Company and Ford Instrument Company.

Satellite!

By

ERIK BERGAUST

and

WILLIAM BELLER

Foreword by
Professor Hermann Oberth

HANOVER HOUSE

GARDEN CITY, NEW YORK

To Jean and Joan

FOREWORD

"Good Heavens, does this mean that I have to read and write some more? When I cannot even find time to read and write enough during normal working hours!" This is what I thought when I received the manuscript for this book in the mail, accompanied by a beautiful letter in which the authors reminded me that three months earlier I had promised, in a weak moment, to read this manuscript and write the foreword.

However, the more I read of this book, the less I objected to having given my promise. The book is highly interesting. And complete! I found information in this book that I had been seeking in vain in hundreds of papers and reports. Consequently, I have learned much from reading the book; now I also know how and where to seek further information for further research in rocketry and astronautics.

How have these authors been able to compile all this material?

We—the so-called experts—who work with rockets every day dare not speak much of developments. Recently a newspaperman looked me up for an interview. The head of the Public Information Office and a security officer from Redstone Arsenal were careful enough to be present during my talk with the reporter. In the course of the conversation, the reporter asked me if it were true that the designers of the V–2 rocket had had great difficulties and many problems with the steering fins and the graphite vanes of that rocket. Before giving him an answer I checked with the two Redstone officials to see whether I could tell the reporter anything about the gimbaled, or swiveling, motor. Both refused to let me say a single word. I did confirm to the newspaperman that it was true that we did have difficulties with the V–2 steering, "but we have overcome the difficulties you mentioned. I am not able to tell you more."

It was on the tip of my tongue to say: "Soon there will be a book written by Erik Bergaust and William Beller, and among the many things described and explained in this book is the operation and function of a gimbaled rocket engine, explained in a manner that makes it fascinating reading for the layman."

Certainly, the material in this book is not restricted or classified.

Most details have been expressed or explained at one time or another by experts, or the information has been released unintentionally and is not considered secret any more. What a tremendous amount of thorough study has gone into this compilation of news and technical reports! Equally fascinating is the know-how and expert handling with which these authors have treated this material, and the way they have interpreted all news correctly and objectively.

This book is exactly what the layman wants. By reading this book he will better understand and interpret the individual news items about satellite and rocket science without getting a false picture of the art. For those who are particularly interested in tomorrow's space flight, I warmly recommend this book. First of all, however, the reader who has *not* been fascinated by or interested in the science of astronautics should read this book. It is seen that space flight is no longer a fantasy of children and lunatics. Rather, humanity is faced with the great and serious growth of a new science. More than 70 years ago a well-known physicist said: "Tomorrow man will even use electricity for lighting. But it is difficult to prove!" Half a century ago in a restaurant at Lindau at the Bodensee, a waiter arrogantly told me, while pointing at Count Zeppelin: "Look at him! There goes that crazy man who wants to fly."

It certainly seems that one should never close his eyes to the promising advances of science, unless one would want to offer a statement that would make him look foolish a few years later. The future of rocket science is fantastic, yet realistic. If it were at all possible for our forefathers, say of four or five generations back, to revisit the Earth today and experience the effects of our technological gains, they would probably think that it was all fantasy created by mad minds. If our ancestors could just take a look at today's New York at night, they would probably get this feeling of unrealistic evolution and technological advancement. And yet there is nothing more realistic than this great city. Likewise, this book contains no descriptions or predictions that will not be realized in the field of rocketry and space flight in the foreseeable future.

I visualize this book as a most useful vocational aid for this country's schools. This book will have great value to a good many people other than engineers, physicists, chemists and geophysicists; in particular, all our high school and college students should read this book.

The science of astronautics is actually built on quite simple principles that we encounter in our everyday living. But it is difficult for us to realize them. If we tie these fundamentals together and analyze them in view of the unusual conditions that are to be found in space, we arrive at some surprising conditions. They embrace new domains of knowledge and know-how, representing the newest kind of wisdom since Aristotle. High school and college students, who are often praying that their lengthy lessons be cut, will become aware of the new world that is awaiting conquest; they will be hypnotized by every word their teachers will utter about space flight. Is it really true that the immediate tomorrow will hold such challenges for these students? Are there any challenging conquests left to modern man, who no longer can go to the Indians for adventure? Astronautics will embrace so many fields that students will become interested in the individual subjects that make up this great new science, such as are outlined and described in this book and such as I have written a book about that will be published shortly. I hope that some day the many individual scientific fields that make up astronautics will be inspiring enough to students that they will decide to become engineers, scientists and technicians.

Society would profit from such an educational trend. As the authors of this book have correctly concluded, we are short of these scientists—the men that are needed to tailor tomorrow's interplanetary travel. This shortage applies to practically every field of science; and from a greater emphasis on rocket engineering our entire area of technology will profit. When one has tasted the science of astronautics, one will soon discover that there are numerous scientific fields connected with it, although they may not all require establishment of a laboratory on the Moon. Of my former students, quite a few have become engineers because I briefed them on satellite and rocket science. Only a few of these engineers worked on rockets, but they have been able to use their rocket knowledge in other scientific fields. And these students are all doing very well.

After having read this book, I feel how ridiculously shortsighted the rivalry between certain individual nations is, which can be eliminated through international co-operation and understanding of technological fields such as space flight. Realizing the many aspects of astronautics, which will break down the barriers between nations and permit science to advance and utilize talents of all countries, let us hope that people will soon agree that there is enough work for everyone, if only the work is rightly distributed.

HERMANN OBERTH

Huntsville, Alabama
March 27, 1956

CONTENTS

INTRODUCTION

The Earth satellites developed under Project *Vanguard* are to be the first space vehicles. The prime purpose of these vehicles will be to derive basic data about the environment in which we live. Yet this is only the short view.

The longer view may easily rank in significance with the first steam vessel in 1802, the first railroad in 1825, and the first airplane in 1903. Each of these radical inventions basically altered ways of life. It is probable that space flight will do no less. The orbiting vehicles can affect nearly every human activity, ranging from the discovery of new medicines to the development of new literature and philosophies. They can help to bring about a universal peace or a universal chaos.

This book is mostly concerned with the utility of space satellites and the way this aspect can affect every person on Earth. We start with the evolution of small instrumented satellites and their power plants. From here we describe the constituents of "empty" space—the natural environment of space vehicles. We look inside satellites to examine their instruments. From these simple beginnings stems the satellites' usefulness. We can see them giving us long-range weather forecasts, improving our communication and transportation systems, helping us discover underground treasures, influencing military tactics, and questioning many theories.

The first practical application of artificial Earth satellites will be during the International Geophysical Year (IGY) 1957–58, an interval set aside for intensive study of the Earth and its surroundings. After the IGY, larger satellites may be built, ones that carry animals aloft—and, finally, man.

Lastly, we summarize the thousands of job opportunities connected with satellite science and point out the paths that men with vision can follow to succeed in what has been called "the last great adventure of man."

In writing this book, we have become indebted to many fine organizations and individuals for their aid in giving us data and keeping us on course. Most of their directions we have followed. But the satellite field is broad and the paths are many. In some cases we have ventured down new ones, but with full knowledge of having been forewarned.

For their help we particularly want to express our sincere gratitude to the U. S. National Committee for the International Geophysical Year, National Academy of Sciences; to the American Rocket Society; and to the Office of Naval Research. We are most grateful to the General Electric Company, Schenectady, New York, without whose kind co-operation we could not have been able to include many of the illustrations; we appreciate their patience with us even under the pressure of tight deadlines. We are also thankful to Martin, Baltimore, who provided the inspiration for several of the sketches.

We would not have been able to produce this book had it not been for the valuable and unstinting assistance of many individuals. Foremost among these are Thomas C. Irvine, News Bureau, General Electric Company; Joseph M. Rowland, Manager of Information Services, Martin, Baltimore; Holt McAloney, Director of Public Relations, Ford Instrument Company; Fred Hamlin, Publisher of *Aero Digest*; Dr. Wernher von Braun, Technical Director, Redstone Arsenal; Andrew G. Haley, Director, American Rocket Society; Dr. E. Homer Newell, Jr., Head of Rocket Sonde Division, and Kurt R. Stehling, Head of Propulsion Section, Vehicle Branch, Naval Research Laboratory; Alexander Satin and Commander George Hoover, Air Branch, Office of Naval Research; Commander Patricia Conwell, Office of Public Information, Office of Naval Research; Hugh Odishaw, Executive Secretary of the U. S. National Committee for the IGY; Dr. Donald Michael, National Science Foundation; and the editors of *Collier's*.

Finally, we wish to thank Professor Hermann Oberth who very kindly consented to write the Foreword.

THE AUTHORS

Washington, D.C.
May, 1956

Satellite!

1. Out of This World

Earth is probably not the only planet where life exists. In our own solar system, Venus resembles the Earth in many ways. Our twin planet has an extensive atmosphere, and being closer to the Sun, it has a very hot climate. With powerful telescopes we have observed the heavy layers of clouds drifting across its surface. We have measured the composition of the gases that make up these clouds and of the Venusian atmosphere. We have estimated its density. From these data we conclude that we can land on Venus with vehicles of airplane type, that is, with ships that can descend to the planet's surface in aerodynamic glides.

While the Earth's air contains mainly nitrogen, Venus has a carbon-dioxide atmosphere. There are no strange gases in Venus's atmospheric envelope—no elements that we do not have on Earth. Different types of vegetation certainly can grow and flourish in the Venusian-type air, but whether these types are unlike those on Earth, we do not know. While our atmosphere contains 21 per cent free oxygen, the oxygen on Venus is believed to exist only in combinations of elements such as in carbon dioxide. But as a fish is able to draw oxygen out of water, a Venusian animal might be equipped to separate and use the oxygen in carbon dioxide, or the animal's metabolism might be attuned to thriving on other gases. The only way we can thoroughly explore Venus is to visit it, as our ancestors explored the lands beyond the great oceans, and as our colleagues are currently exploring the antarctic. Since the Venusian atmosphere does not sustain the oxygen-breathing life we know, we must bring air with us, just as a mountain climber must bring a rope to assist him in his ascent.

Mars is perhaps even more romantic than Venus from an explorer's point of view. In the first place, we know much more about Mars than any other planet in the sky; photographs of this small globe show red and green areas that are believed to be high desert plateaus and low regions with vegetation. We believe we can also see the famous canals, a web of lines crisscrossing the surface of the planet. Some scientists think the canals are cracks or narrow valleys through which water is flowing, thereby providing moisture for a more concentrated and elaborate vegetation. Perhaps a higher form of life flourishes in these valleys.

Mars travels around the Sun in 687 days. The seasons there are much like those on Earth; when summer comes to the Northern Hemisphere, winter moves in on the southern half of the planet. With large telescopes we can see the snow melt in the summertime and, at the same time, notice how the green areas become more distinct. With small telescopes, we can see Mars's two tiny moons, Phobos and Deimos. Each of them is quite small compared to our Moon, and for size they can best be compared with two large mountains.

The pull of gravity on Mars is considerably less than that on the Earth; as a matter of fact, a man weighing 180 pounds on Earth would weigh only 68 pounds on Mars.

Soviet astronomers, who have good opportunities for making significant astronomical observations from Alma-Ata and Tashkent, claim that there are no oceans on Mars, that its lakes, if any, are no larger than one twentieth of a square mile. These astronomers say that the Martian atmosphere contains the same amount of oxygen that we have in high mountainous regions on Earth, as in the Himalayas. The atmospheric pressure on Mars is somewhat less than one pound per square inch, as against 14.7 for the Earth. Since Mars is much farther from the Sun than our planet, the temperatures on Mars are lower. Near the planet's equator the temperature may rise to 50 or 60 degrees Fahrenheit at noon.

Still our information about Mars is so meager that we do not know whether life exists there, or whether we would find anything on Mars that would tell us more about the universe. But we shall find out, for Mars is definitely to be visited.

Of course, the first celestial body that we may visit is our own natural satellite. We realize that there is no life on our airless Moon.

Nevertheless, our scientists want to go to the Moon for many technical reasons, and there is no doubt that we shall soon be on our way. The first man-made vehicle landing on the Moon will probably be an instrumented rocket that will crash on the satellite's surface. But we shall also hear of man-made rocket vehicles circumnavigating the Moon and returning to Earth. Automatic cameras will take pictures of the Moon's unseen side.

We have a long scientific climb ahead of us. The Moon, Mars and Venus are far away. Nevertheless, these are the adventures we can look forward to when we see the first *Earth Satellite Vehicle* (ESV) rise in the west. We shall finally have climbed to the first rung; we shall be ready to advance higher toward the greatest of man's achievements—the conquest of space.

The pioneering work is being done now. The use of tiny basketball-size satellites will initiate the new eras and open up wide vistas for science and civilization. These instrumented metallic spheres, orbiting around the earth at 18,000 miles per hour, will affect every man and woman in the world. The effects will range from new kinds of jobs and professions to a raising of our standard of living. We shall experience near-perfect radio transmission and weather forecasting; we shall see amazing conquests in the fields of medicine, physics, chemistry, astronomy and other sciences.

Tomorrow's jet air liners will have in-flight television. Programs in 3–D and color will be relayed to the airplane from outer space. For example, air travelers between Washington and San Francisco will be viewing TV from London; passengers on a transatlantic ocean liner en route from New York to Havre will watch programs from San Francisco. The TV short waves will fly out to small satellites that will relay the programs to receivers on the other side of the globe. By the help of three space satellites in circular orbits, more than 95 per cent of the Earth will be covered, the remaining 5 per cent representing only the polar areas. Similarly, a telephone call from anywhere in the United States to Melbourne, Australia, or Helsinki, Finland, will go via the instrumented, unmanned stations in space.

The days are not far off when a man in Colorado Springs, perhaps, will purchase a television set equipped with a conventional radio dial instead of a channel selector. He will tune his set to watch the Olympic games directly from Melbourne via a man-made moon. He can turn the dial knob slightly to the right or the left and receive programs from Capetown, South Africa, or Rio de Janeiro, Brazil.

Most of the world's countries now co-operate extensively in the field of meteorology. Tomorrow's weather forecasts, when based upon readings transmitted from satellites and incorporated with routine observations from ground stations throughout the world, will teach our meteorologists to forecast weather conditions weeks and months in advance. This certainly will make air travel safer, will revolutionize tourist industries in every country and affect the prices of goods and commodities as well as hotel and travel rates. When everybody knows two months in advance that it will rain and be rather cold in Switzerland during the last three weeks of July, then hotel and travel rates will go down there. The person who does not have any choice about picking his vacation period will benefit from the lower prices if he goes to Switzerland—although he must accept the fact that his vacation will be a rather wet and chilly one.

Of course, accurate and advance weather forecasts have an even greater significance for the world's farmers. It may be that the living standards in certain areas will be favorably affected because of this one aspect of satellite utility alone. There is no reason why a Dakota farmer should grow corn when he knows in advance that Iowa will get the best corn weather it has had in decades.

By and by the world's agriculture standards will change. Markets will become surer, better balanced. The efficiency and stabilization in synchronized agriculture practiced by the farmers of Iowa and Dakota will spread to other states and foreign countries. Competition and output in such fields as cotton production will be affected because the cotton-producing countries will know in advance what the export market will be. If weather is expected to favor one specific country only, the others can put emphasis on other products.

Weather has a tremendous influence on a great many other endeavors—ranging from sports events to whaling and other kinds of fisheries. Advance knowledge of drought and floods will help prevent loss of human lives and millions of dollars' worth of property damage. Advance weather forecasts will even have a bearing on insurance rates. These items do not belong to the distant future; these are utility aspects expected to influence the world during the next 10 to 20 years.

With intensive research and wide use of artificial satellites practically all elements in our present-day way of living will change. We are told that people will soon have a life expectancy of 90 or 100 years. A contributing factor will be the scientific knowledge obtained through *satellite science.*

Satellite science is not a rigor in its own right; it embraces all sciences, giving researchers new ways to attack old problems, new possibilities for studies of phenomena we do not understand, and new methods for experiments that would be incomplete without environmental circumstances such as near-complete vacuum, intense solar exposure and bombardments by other radiations indigenous to space.

We have already sent human brain tissue to 24 miles' altitude. Placed in an air-conditioned balloon-gondola, a human skull, brain and tissue have made a trip into the cold of the upper atmosphere and returned to Earth. The eight-hour trip was undertaken for the USAF Aero Medical Laboratory. Numerous tests will soon determine what the effects of the flight were on the tissue and brain— and whether the skull was punctured by *cosmic dust,* microscopical particles flying about in the universe with speeds so great that one barely visible particle could penetrate a sheet of automobile steel. When a human skull is placed inside a satellite vehicle that circumnavigates the Earth, medical researchers will be able to determine the effects of space radiations on the brain tissue, and on disease bacilli. It has been suggested that a better understanding of certain radiations will help us find a cure for cancer. This success alone would be worth huge grants of money for satellite science.

The first small satellites will be used for determining outer atmospheric densities. They will also be used to obtain more accurate measures of the Earth's equatorial oblateness, of intercontinental distances and other geodetic data. This means that we shall be able to make accurate maps and construct better navigational devices for our ships and airplanes. We shall also investigate the nature and effect of ultraviolet radiations, and the relative abundance of matter, such as hydrogen, in space.

In a satellite equipped with Geiger counters, *cosmic rays* will be studied. These high-speed rays from outer space are not completely understood. Involving the highest energy particles known, the study of cosmic rays is of great interest to the scientist. From a practical point of view, cosmic rays interest the promoters of space flight, for the rays could constitute a potential hazard.

As the source of practically all the energy affecting the Earth and its atmosphere, sunlight is of prime interest and importance. The ultraviolet and other regions of the solar spectrum are absorbed at high altitudes causing photochemical activity, heating and winds. Variations in intensity of the solar radiations are associated with corresponding variations of atmospheric and weather phenomena.

With *photon counters*—sensitive instruments for measuring tiny amounts of electromagnetic energy—the ultraviolet regions of the solar spectrum can be monitored above the atmosphere which absorbs these ultraviolet waves. In particular, the opportunity will exist to observe the ultraviolet light curve of the Sun during the occurrence of solar flares.

Interplanetary space is not a complete vacuum. Its actual density is not definitely known, although the figure of one atom per cubic centimeter (0.06 cubic inch) has been used. The data on which this estimate is based are meager; to provide a better estimate will be the object of some of the satellite experiments. It might be possible to observe the Sun directly by means of photon counters, and simultaneously to observe radiation emanating from some direction other than that of the Sun. By correlating the intensities observed directly from the Sun with those observed at an angle, it should be possible to estimate the average density of hydrogen atoms in space.

While most of us must wait to feel the many effects of satellite science, some people have already been touched. Thousands of engineers are being hired every month by those aircraft manufacturers working in the field of satellite flight. The first basketball satellites have already been bypassed by more courageous designs now on the drawing boards. The guided-missile and rocket divisions of practically every major airplane builder now include departments devoted to satellite and space-flight projects. The job opportunities are many and fascinating.

The most obvious evidence of this new engineering development has brought a klondike type of rush to central Florida. A migration of 100,000 people is predicted for this state within the next few years. These include not only engineers but also plumbers, carpenters, milkmen, hotel managers, gasoline-station operators, lawyers, dentists, and others with ancillary interests in the satellite. Real estate values have risen spectacularly near Patrick Air Force Base, chosen as the launching site for the first satellites. This migration is a direct result of rockets and satellites. This base, located near Cocoa Beach, southeast of Orlando, has become Satellite City, U.S.A.

Scientists and military personnel travel between Washington and Patrick AFB every day. Meetings are being held constantly, for there is much planning to do. The Air Research and Development Command is responsible for the Patrick facility and for the Bahamas Missile Range, a chain of island observation and instrumentation posts stretching from Patrick via Grand Bahama Island, Eleutria, San Salvador, Mayaguana, Grand Turk, Dominican Republic, Puerto Rico, St. Lucia to the Ascension Island in the Atlantic Ocean, near Africa. Several thousand personnel are stationed on these islands. Their job is to track rockets and missiles as they zoom eastward over the Atlantic Ocean. Pan American World Airways, which has wide experience in operating air bases, was awarded the contract for running the Bahama range stations; the Radio Corporation of America is handling the technical tracking job.

Some of the people have lived on the range for several years. They will never go back to the mainland for a different job. In the warm and healthy climate, they live inexpensively, and since they earn high salaries, have free room and board, 30 days' vacation a year and free transportation whenever they visit the mainland, one cannot blame them. One couple on Grand Bahama Island pay only $35 a year to the British Government for lease of the land on which they have built their $1,800 rambler. They have no other expenses, no taxes, no household costs. Besides, they earn up to 50 per cent more than they would in similar positions in the United States. There are all types of job openings. This rocket and satellite enterprise will last for many, many years. To these people, the guided missile has been a blessing—soon their work will embrace the whole area of space flight.

Who are these people? Some are bulldozer drivers, some run cafeterias, some handle laundries, some operate fire engines, some watch high-flying rockets in radarscopes. Modern living quarters are being erected, as well as motion-picture houses, clubs and gymnasiums. On Grand Bahama Island, several hundred PAA and RCA people are working intensively to be prepared for the future large-scale missile and satellite operations. Only a few years from now there will be a population of 10,000 on this island.

There could be no satellites without a formidable rocket technology and a vast fund of missile science experience. We can now build small or large satellites in our laboratories. We can put highly sensitive instruments into them, and we can test the finished unit to find out whether it will work. The construction of a small satellite designed for telemetering data from the upper atmosphere or from space is no more complicated than manufacturing radios and television sets. Artificial satellites may be made on a mass-production basis, if necessary. After all, they are only little lightweight metal spheres containing instruments and electronic gear. But the question of putting a satellite into an orbit outside the Earth's atmosphere is a quite different story.

Highly advanced rockets are needed for this task. The guidance and stabilization gear of these rockets must operate with near-perfect accuracy. The flow of propellants into the rocket engines must be synchronized to split-second precision. A task force of engineers and technicians is needed for launching and tracking a satellite rocket. Complex ground facilities are required, including such service units as weather stations, communication centers, radar and camera observation posts, laboratories, fire departments—even field hospitals where men can be treated for injuries such as burns from liquid oxygen.

Such systems are currently in use at every guided-missile facility; and since there is overlapping experience between weapon systems and designing, building, handling and launching satellite vehicles, the knowledge we have gathered is highly useful. The engineers who design and build engines for our missiles are being asked to make the engines for satellite rockets. The relationship between satellite science and the *intercontinental ballistic missile* is so close that the over-all construction, launching and guidance techniques are almost identical.

The intercontinental ballistic missile has been referred to as the ultimate weapon—if one will grant that there can be such an instrument. Present concepts define these weapons quite clearly. In the clipped terminology of aeronautical engineers they are known as *ICBM*, which is a guided missile so powerful and accurate that it could bomb New York from Moscow (or vice versa) in little more than an hour.

Fitted with a nuclear-fission warhead, such missiles would travel at an estimated speed of 8,000 to 16,000 miles an hour, a velocity so great that any defense against them would be exceedingly difficult. It is for this reason that the ICBM, when it is made operational, might be unbeatable.

While very little factual information has been released about this country's work on the ICBMs, the U.S. versions so far are known as Convair's SM–65, or *Atlas,* and Martin's *Titan.* Companies like Douglas and General Electric are also working on ICBMs.

A missile such as the *Atlas* will take off vertically from a special platform, under the impetus of multiple rocket motors in its lower section. Soon the missile will begin to tilt. At about 15 miles' altitude, the first section will drop away. Another set of rocket motors in the middle section will push the now smaller missile still higher. About 100 miles above the Earth, the second section will drop away, and the final portion, about 30 feet long and 4 feet in diameter, will hurtle through the upper atmosphere as a ballistic shell.

These weapons are indicative of the development trends in missile science today—only 30 years after Dr. Robert Goddard fired his liquid-fuel rocket to an altitude of 41 feet. It traveled a distance of 220 feet and reached a velocity of 60 miles per hour.

Since then rocketry has become a science of its own. We are on the threshold of a new aeronautical age—not characterized by adjectives such as supersonic or atomic but by the headings Missiles and Satellites. There is no doubt that the theoretical possibilities of the guided missile in warfare has made it imperative to establish a guided-missile industry. Scientists and engineers in general have become enthusiastic over this development because extraordinary challenges are involved, and persons of imagination and creative talent cannot help being fascinated.

Since the German V–2s were aimed at London in 1944, speeding many times as fast as the sound of their coming, their military importance has been obvious. This lesson was clearly understood by every military nation. Even before the first atomic bomb, it took little imagination to picture dozens of deadly duties that missiles could perform. And if they had carried atomic warheads, they would have reduced much of England to radioactive rubble.

But the missiles of World War II were not dependable. Effective missiles call for a technology that did not exist at that time; new production methods were needed. Better rocket motors, more reliable and disentangled electronics, more intelligent computers and more sensitive instruments were demanded. New metals, ceramics and high-velocity propellants were required. Furthermore, adequate guidance techniques had to evolve. The answering of these needs has resulted in more dependable rocket motors, considerably lighter and enormously more powerful. The electronic computers, the brains of the missiles, have grown rapidly in capability.

A missile's tiny gyros, bearings and electronic components must be manufactured with superwatchmaker's precision. The job is sometimes done in a windowless factory. Since no speck of dust can be tolerated, the air is changed by fans and filters every few minutes, and positive air pressure is maintained inside the building so that any air leakage will be outward, not inward. Engineers in the drafting rooms are forbidden to tear paper or use pencil erasers as both make dust, and all employees are required to wear nylon smocks. Physically handicapped men and women who are used to sitting long hours without unnecessary motion are said to be among the best assembly workers.

It is a historical phenomenon, although not a strange one, that the development of rockets and, in particular, intercontinental missiles —of their power plants and airframes as well as their instruments and warheads—has led into satellite science.

Dr. Eugen Sänger, rocket pioneer and first president of the International Astronautical Federation, says that humanity may soon be in the dilemma of declaring war nonsensical—not only on moral, but also on technical grounds—and at the same time be faced with the problem of trying to avoid dropping the gigantic defense organizations of research and industry, as well as of the military establishments. The most natural way out of this dilemma seems to be satellite science. Satellite science and space flight will far better satisfy the urge for adventure, for discharging vitality, for reaching new horizons than does our present-day military aviation. It will require research institutes, industries and military organizations for its implementation. Yet, by this virtue, space flight will accomplish cultural tasks instead of threatening humanity. Looking into the future, we see rockets used logistically in building artificial satellites, we see nuclear rockets on interplanetary research missions—and one day we may even see atomic-powered vehicles speeding across the farthest reaches of the universe. To accomplish these tasks, we shall require sound development programs employing the best scientists and the best engineers. Maybe Patrick AFB, from being a military establishment, one day will have become a giant scientific center for peaceful space-flight operations. If people become space-minded in the sense that they understand the vast scientific possibilities of cosmic flight, the dream of peace may become a reality.

It is interesting to note that more than 30 years ago, the father of space flight, Hermann Oberth, revealed plans for building entire stations in space. At that time, few people took his ideas seriously. But Professor Oberth could prove mathematically that satellites or space platforms could be constructed. One of the most remarkable aspects suggested by Oberth at that time was the *space mirror* concept. A huge mirror in space would reflect the Sun's radiation in focused beams, its utility aspects including heating and illuminating cities. It could also be used to "boil" the water of our oceans, which in turn would yield vapor and rain during drought periods. Considered seriously by many scientists today, the space mirror was first suggested in 1923.

It has been stressed on numerous occasions during the last decade that the achievement of space flight will require fantastic sums of money, amounts that would strain the budgets of even the largest nations. If we talk in terms of large manned-space-station systems, it might be that the solution will be found in global collaboration, and such space projects require an almost perfect level of world peace.

Dr. Walter Dornberger, formerly commanding general of Nazi Germany's famous Rocket Test Station, Peenemünde, and now Missile Design Consultant for Bell Aircraft, has said that it is likely that only military reasons could ever muster the vast sums needed for space flight, and that the initial phases of a space-flight program— such as establishing an unmanned satellite and, secondly, launching of manned space ships—could be carried out only on the basis of military advantage. Landing on the Moon and planets would be difficult to sell to the taxpaying public on any grounds. After all, what possible practical advantage could be demonstrated?

Dr. Dornberger believes that the constriction induced by building solely for military purposes impedes the thinking of the backers of interplanetary travel. The military engineer deals with hardware and is walled about by secrecy. This secrecy frustrates the space-flight theorist, whose lot is hard enough even with adequate practical data, and he must content himself with topics that in many cases must strike the casual observer as academic trivia. This situation is not likely to change for a long time, but Dr. Dornberger feels that if it did, the theorist could jump ahead about 30 or 50 years, and perform many valuable studies from the viewpoint of space flight as a *fait accompli.*

We do not entirely agree with Dr. Dornberger. The amount of money needed for the first small satellites has been estimated at $35 million. It is quite likely that more money will be spent on these satellites indirectly, but definitely not as much as $100 million, as has been suggested by many. Also, it is established that the first satellites will not have any active military advantage, although some of the data gathered could be useful for ICBM development.

We feel that the taxpayers will not suffer because of these satellites. The projects will not upset the U.S. national budget, or any other budget. The United States certainly can manage to pay for the first American satellite, and the Soviet government for theirs.

The research contributing to the satellites has been accomplished as a by-product of other projects—largely military. The Department of Defense works hand in hand with the various scientific institutions involved in the project. We do look forward to the time when some of our scientific talent can be released from the defense task —when the country can afford the manpower and money required to tackle an over-all space-flight program.

There is no reason why we shall not all benefit from the conquest of space. "The knowledge we will have to gain," says Milton W. Rosen, technical director of the Earth Satellite Vehicle *Vanguard* project, "the techniques we will have to master, the machines we will have to build—all will bring more material benefit to the Earth's population than any gold or uranium we may find on Mars or Venus. The value of space flight is in the doing of it."

2. Planning for the Orbiters

We have been close to realizing space flight before now. On December 29, 1948, in a report to Congress, the late Secretary of Defense James V. Forrestal mentioned that a study for construction of artificial space satellites was proceeding. But the so-called *Forrestal Project* soon died.

We were perhaps too optimistic at that time, although optimism is an important ingredient of any philosophy of action. So is caution. The American Rocket Society's Space Flight Committee had both these characteristics in a report they published in 1952, which considered the possibilities and types of action needed to promote space flight. In agreement with the Rocket Society's proposal was a paper presented in 1953 by A. V. Cleaver, a leading British rocket expert and former chairman of the British Interplanetary Society. Mr. Cleaver's work had a great influence on the thinking of our own experts. In brief, he suggested that the first phase of a space program be theoretical and applied work resulting in the establishment of an unmanned satellite. Then we might tackle the operation of a regular manned satellite and achieve some occasional circumlunar flights. Finally, he visualized landings on the Moon and the nearest planets, and return to Earth.

In the American Rocket Society's Journal, the prominent rocket pioneer G. Edward Pendray wrote that World War II brought the society its greatest opportunity—and its greatest hazard. Rockets were being developed wholesale, and rocketry almost overnight was becoming a major industry. "The opportunity presented to the society by all this was growth and leadership; but the hazard was that, among the hundreds of new rocket technologists entering the field, the society was relatively unknown.

"And unfortunately to some who did know of it, its technical reputation was not what they felt it should be. For the American Rocket Society (ARS), which had been kept alive these many years by the magic of the interplanetary idea, now stood in danger of extinction because of association with that very idea. Interplanetary flight was still not technologically respectable in the 1940s in many quarters."

This danger had been recognized as far back as 1934, when the society—at that time called the American Interplanetary Society— was renamed the American Rocket Society. As the editor of *Astronautics* explained at the time: "In the opinion of many members, adoption of the more conservative name, while in no way implying that we have abandoned the interplanetary idea, will attract able members repelled by the present name."

The significance of this resolution is important. As the approach to space flight became more realistic, and more evident—because of gains in rocket technology—the more careful and conservative the ARS became. As a result, the ARS managed to advance thinking along the line of a scientific and peaceful conquest of space. The society, consequently, became the spark plug that ignited the space-satellite idea. Its work had a tremendous influence on the National Science Foundation when that institution had to decide whether artificial satellites were to be recommended.

For several years the American Rocket Society members had tried to convince the various scientific institutions that satellite flight was feasible. In 1953, the chairman of the ARS Space Flight Committee invited Alan T. Waterman, director of the National Science Foundation, to attend a plenary meeting of the committee. Soon thereafter, a confidential report was issued, which stated that the Space Flight Committee proposed that the "National Science Foundation study the utility of an unmanned satellite vehicle to science, commerce and industry, and national defense. Such a study should precede any considerations of feasibility and cost, which could be undertaken if the utility study showed a definite need for a satellite vehicle."

The committee stated that "examples of these research uses might be: for a superior astronomical observatory site; for biological and chemical research utilizing nongravity conditions; for electronic research utilizing a more perfect vacuum of unlimited size for microwave research in free space, cosmic ray, and nuclear research, etc."

In 1954 the committee submitted to the National Science Foundation an open proposal "On the Utility of an Artificial Unmanned Earth Satellite." The text stated that the study of the utility of an unmanned Earth satellite would be one of the most important steps that could be taken immediately to advance the cause of space flight, and that this step would also increase the country's scientific knowledge.

Why call for an unmanned Earth satellite? Although many satellite proposals had been suggested, the small unmanned satellite is the only one for which feasibility could be shown right now. This opinion was held by many responsible engineers and scientists involved in rocket and guided-missile work and in upper-atmospheric research. Most of these people agreed that the unmanned Earth satellite would be the first step toward more ambitious undertakings.

Why study utility? Although many claims had been made for the utility of a satellite vehicle and many uses had been proposed, the subject had not been investigated by a responsible organization and had not rested upon a broad foundation.

Because of recent advances in guided missiles, the cost of producing an unmanned satellite is not the mammoth sum that was at one time considered necessary. Nevertheless, the creation of even a small satellite is still a major undertaking, and does require a modest expenditure which must be justified. The Rocket Society felt that to build a satellite merely for the purpose of saying it had been done would not justify the cost. Rather, the satellite should serve useful purposes—purposes that would command the respect of the officials who sponsored it, the scientists and engineers who produced it, and the community that paid for it. The society therefore recommended that the study of utility be considered one of the most important tasks to be accomplished prior to building a satellite.

It was apparent to the Rocket Society's Space Flight Committee during their early deliberations that the subject of utility could not be entirely divorced from feasibility, and that some concept of feasibility would have to be assumed. This was done not to be restrictive, but to provide a frame of reference from which those investigators considering utility could proceed. It was assumed that it would be feasible to establish a small pay load in an orbit, the difficulty increasing with the size of the pay load, and with the means that could be provided for communicating information from the satellite to the Earth. With this concept in mind, the committee outlined the various fields of utility, such as astronomy and astrophysics, biology, communications, geodesy, geophysics and many other ones arising from the unusual environment of space flight.

Since it was established in 1946, the Office of Naval Research (ONR) has been engaged in supporting basic research—the starting point for every major technical development. Its concern with basic research has necessarily included development of the research tools needed to make these new advances. The scientific frontiers that now confront man are so remote from his usual environment that he cannot explore them without tools of much greater complexity than any he has used in his progress thus far. Development of the tools demands a great deal of difficult and expensive research.

ONR has had a strong program of upper-atmospheric research for many years, in fact, the organization was a pioneer in the field. Its primary concern was for the accumulation of scientific knowledge, since we have to progress scientifically if we are to meet the military requirements of the future. During the past few years, ONR has supported work on high-altitude aircraft, such as the two Douglas *Skyrocket* research planes. It became apparent that aircraft research and development was leading to the point where man would eventually be able to fly an aircraft beyond the atmosphere, into space. ONR realized that science did not have the information about these regions needed to permit such flight. In particular, more accurate data on air density, pressure and temperature were needed. The big problem in this type of research is how to get up very high and stay there. ONR knew that their present methods of gathering data through rockets and balloons were not good enough. Some means had to be found for gathering data over extended periods. After looking over the possible research tools, ONR agreed that the only solution appeared to be the development of an Earth satellite that could stay above the Earth for a long while, especially when compared with rockets or balloons—and relay information back. Although satellite vehicles had been repeatedly proposed, studied and rejected, ONR felt that the need for continuing long-range research and development required an evaluation of the satellite's technical abilities in terms of current and future needs.

On June 23, 1954, shortly after the first detailed satellite proposals had been submitted by the Rocket Society, a telephone call to the Office of Naval Research from Frederick C. Durant III, president of the International Astronautical Federation, disclosed that the famous missile expert and space-flight enthusiast Dr. Wernher von Braun would be in Washington within the next few days. Chief Engineer of ONR's Air Branch, Alexander Satin, and Commander George W. Hoover of that office decided to hold a conference to discuss the subject of satellites to determine how best to set up a research program.

Two days later a historical meeting was held in one of the Navy buildings in Washington. In attendance were Dr. Wernher von Braun; Fred Durant; Harvard astronomer Dr. Fred L. Whipple; Dr. Fred Singer, member of the Physics Department, University of Maryland; Mr. David Young of Aerojet-General Corporation; Commander George Hoover, and other ONR personnel including Alexander Satin.

When the meeting was opened, the first question placed before the group was whether any scientific satellite project was being studied in the light of the type of research that ONR needed. After considerable discussion of projects dealing with very-high-altitude research, it was agreed that although many investigations were being conducted, there was no specific satellite program under way.

The second question was whether it was possible to launch a satellite within the next few years. At this point, Dr. von Braun suggested the possibility of using a combination of *Redstone* and *Loki* missiles to push the satellite into an orbit outside the Earth's atmosphere. He explained that the *Redstone* missile, a highly advanced V–2-type rocket, might be used as a main booster on which could be mounted a multiple cluster of *Loki* solid-propellant rockets.

After considerable detailed explanation by von Braun, it was concluded that such a program was possible—providing an official project could be established and Army participation effected, since the *Redstone* was an Army missile.

The discussion continued with Dr. Singer pointing out the need for relatively heavy pay loads, and also the desirability of orbits that would permit as much information as possible to be gathered. Fred Durant listed the technological advancements that could be made through the use of an Earth satellite. Dr. Whipple sketched the major areas where new information could be obtained. By making the satellite vehicle visible by means of optical and electronic means, he said that it would be possible to investigate the phenomena connected with *ionization,* the effects of electrically charged particles in the atmosphere. He also suggested that the decay from an elliptical to a circular orbit of the satellite could tell us much about the density of air at extreme altitudes.

It was believed by those present that the program suggested by Dr. Singer was a definite step in the search for upper-air data, but that this must be considered a second phase. It was agreed that enough information could be obtained from a minimum satellite, weighing perhaps five pounds, to warrant proceeding with the first step in a large satellite program.

Even a five-pound satellite was thought to be difficult enough to get into an orbit. The venture certainly would require skillfully planned launching and tracking methods. It would be a challenging task. But it could be done, and it could be done within a much shorter time than would be required for a fully instrumented vehicle.

There were many possible methods and many rocket combinations that could be used to place the satellite in an orbit, but the *Redstone-Loki* combination was at that time an arrangement capable of putting a satellite into an orbit without calling for major development work.

Following the meeting—which was the first phase of the American satellite project—a presentation was made to the Chief of Naval Research. He gave official approval for further investigation of the project, and authorized conversation with the Army's Redstone Arsenal in Huntsville, Alabama.

On August 3, 1954, Navy representatives visited Redstone and a meeting was held with General H. N. Toftoy and Dr. von Braun. After some discussion regarding the possibility of using the *Redstone-Loki* combination, General Toftoy said that Redstone would co-operate providing General Lesley Simon, at that time Chief of Army Ordnance, approved of the participation.

In the sequence of events, General Toftoy went to Washington for a discussion with General Simon, who said he would co-operate with the Navy provided the project would not slow down the Army's missile weapons programs, and provided it would not draw excessively upon the Army's missile engineering manpower. The Chief of

Naval Research was then notified, and ONR's Air Branch was given permission to proceed with preliminary studies leading to the establishment of a detailed program. Commander Hoover was assigned to the post of Project Officer. *Project Orbiter* became the code name of the program. It was classified CONFIDENTIAL.

The Navy was to handle the design, development and construction of the satellite, which included arranging for tracking facilities, logistic support, and recording and interpreting the scientific data. The Army agreed to carry the responsibility for the over-all design, construction, and launching of the satellite vehicle. It is worth noting that while the Navy supported the satellite studies in order to obtain more data about the upper atmosphere for future high-altitude missile and airplane flights, the Air Force was not even involved in the project.

Three contracts were let immediately by ONR. The visibility study was given to Varo Manufacturing Company, who hired Dr. Whipple as a consultant. Alabama Engineering & Tool Company was awarded the second contract; this study was to embrace the design and development of the *Loki* cluster mount and guidance system needed to place the satellite in an orbit. The third study contract was given to the Aerophysics Corporation. This company was to conduct development of the *Loki* cluster. A fourth contract was planned for International Business Machines Corporation, which was to study the communication aspect.

One problem that became evident quite early in the study was that of logistic support. Men and equipment would have to be transported to locations practically all around the globe. From material released by the Navy on *Project Orbiter* there is no indication that any existing base—Army, Navy or Air Force—was considered as a launching site; such a site had to be constructed, as well as tracking stations. Enough supplies had to be made available for the crews to operate for many days and perhaps even a year. For this reason, a presentation was made to the Chief of Naval Operations. His only remark was: "Tell us what you want moved and where you want it moved, and we'll see that it gets there."

On January 20, 1955, the proposed program was submitted to the Assistant Secretary of Defense in charge of Research and Development, as the first step in bringing the project to the attention of the Secretary of Defense—and, eventually, to the President of the United

States. Five meetings of the *Orbiter* team were held in all, the last one on May 23 and 24, 1955, at Redstone Arsenal and Patrick Air Force Base, to witness the firing of a giant *Redstone* missile. Important decisions were made as a result of these meetings.

The people involved became busy now, because the program was beginning to take form. An equatorial orbit was considered best for the first satellite. Later a polar orbit and an inclined orbit would be tried. The Naval Research Laboratory, which had some interesting satellite ideas of its own, was asked to participate and submit a backup program. The use of *Minitrack*, a highly sensitive electronic missile tracking apparatus, was offered by NRL. Representatives of the contractors were frequent visitors to Washington; conference after conference was held in Mr. Satin's and Commander Hoover's offices. Dr. von Braun was traveling back and forth between Washington and Huntsville. To him, the satellite project was a personal victory. Since 1930 he had tried to convince the world that satellites could and should be built. He had devoted his whole life to such studies and had at one time been arrested and jailed by the Gestapo in Germany for suggesting that the Nazi rocket research work would one day be applied to the peaceful conquest of space.

In April, 1955, ONR began the planning of an expedition for establishing a launching site. The expedition was scheduled to leave in the spring of 1957, with the understanding that the actual launching of the first satellite would be undertaken by midsummer or fall of that year. But as ONR was planning for the first satellite expedition, an entirely different and unknown (to ONR) satellite project was revealed by the President of the United States—an instrumented satellite would be launched to gather scientific information which in turn would be distributed to scientists of all the world's countries.

Scientific and technological break-throughs often come in pairs. The universality of science frequently leads widely separated groups and individuals to arrive at almost identical ideas at the same time. While ONR was studying their *Orbiter* and its importance for high-altitude-flight research, the National Science Foundation had proceeded to accept the initial proposals by the Rocket Society. The Defense Department had been asked to encourage the "scientific" satellite, and the President of the United States enthusiastically had approved of the venture. Obviously, the *Orbiter* project could be canceled, since some of the basic information sought by ONR could be expected to result from the other satellite. So *Project Orbiter* was nudged out by *Project Vanguard*.

A new approach was now in the undertaking. Everything had to be reorganized, and the pioneers and the original backers of the satellite idea, such as Dr. von Braun, Alexander Satin, George Hoover, Fred Durant and others, were almost forgotten.

The revelation of *Project Vanguard* came as follows: on the morning of July 29, 1955, White House Press Secretary, James C. Hagerty, told newsmen that there would be a story of "some importance" given out at 1:30 P.M. When the time arrived, reporters were steered into a conference room which, back in the Roosevelt and Truman days, was known as the "Fish Room." Here they found Hagerty at a table with several prominent scientists from the National Science Foundation and the National Academy of Sciences.

Secretary Hagerty announced that President Eisenhower had approved plans for launching an Earth-circling satellite. The President had expressed his personal satisfaction that the American project would provide scientific data that would be made available to all countries, the Soviet Union included. He stressed that the satellite would be constructed strictly for scientific purposes, and not with any war purpose in mind, although the Department of Defense would help with the project.

The reporters then began firing questions at the scientists. Did the announcement, one asked, mean that the United States really was capable of putting up a satellite?

"Of course," said Dr. Waterman. The scientists had no doubt that all the problems could be worked out.

The wires of the world's news bureaus and press agencies flashed the news to every corner of the globe. As an almost immediate reply to the American announcement came the *United Press* dispatch from Moscow stating that the Soviet Union was preparing to launch a similar satellite.

The Eisenhower announcement was followed by more complete statements by the scientists involved. According to Detlov W. Bronk, president of the National Academy of Sciences and Alan T. Waterman, director of the National Science Foundation, the *Vanguard* project calls for the construction of a small, unmanned, Earth-circling satellite vehicle to be used for basic scientific observations during the *International Geophysical Year* (IGY), the period set aside from July 1, 1957, to December 31, 1958, for world-wide observations in the fields of the Earth sciences by about 42 nations. The satellite project is sponsored by these two organizations as part of the United States program of participation in the IGY.

The stimulant for such a vehicle was provided, as we have seen, by the American Rocket Society. The final decision was based upon a resolution passed by the Special Committee for the International Geophysical Year, and because of ONR's *Orbiter* program and long interest and experience in the broad aspects of upper-atmospheric research, the Chief of Naval Research was selected to manage the Defense Department portion of the *Vanguard* satellite program.

Project Vanguard is a three-year project. According to the Martin Company of Baltimore, prime contractor for the project, it is a 6,000-man-hour job. ONR and its agency NRL are using, as contractors or consultants, "nearly all" the nation's leading scientific authorities in geophysics, astrophysics and rocket research.

Since the Earth satellite problem differs in several respects from the bulk of NRL's work, the project is being prosecuted outside the division structure of the laboratory. A separate project office reporting directly to the Laboratory Director of Research has been established. It was not felt necessary or desirable to set up a large, complex organization to co-ordinate the project. Much of the necessary co-ordination of the technical program could be carried out on a day-to-day basis by scientists and engineers at the working level in the Navy, the other services and industry.

The Army and the Air Force (who came into the satellite program after it was begun) have designated *Project Vanguard* liaison officers who have official responsibility for keeping their services abreast of the status of the project, and who have kept ONR and NRL workers informed of their services' potential for participation in any given phase of the work. For many years, the Army, Navy and Air Force military and civilian personnel involved in rocketry and other aspects of upper-atmospheric research have used formal machinery and informal contacts for working out mutual problems. This same working-level communication network, although it has caused some confusion at times, is also used to attack problems that must be solved before the *Vanguard* satellite can be launched.

The Navy's approach to the management of *Project Vanguard* has been shaped by the project's mission, which is threefold:

First, a satellite is to be placed in an orbit during the IGY.

Second, proof of such an achievement must be established by defining the orbit. This means tracking the satellite and providing information by which observers in the United States and other countries can also detect and track it.

Third, it must be possible to perform at least one experiment of recognized scientific merit. "We hope to make a precise measurement of the density of air in outer space, the detection of hydrogen in space or radiation from the Sun, or something of equal scientific importance," according to Admiral N. Furth, former Chief of Naval Research.

These then are the three primary technical responsibilities that must be discharged by NRL. But they cannot be done without assistance from the Army, Air Force and American science and industry.

Before long, several countries will be launching their satellites, and the need for international co-operation in the various areas of satellite science will become increasingly evident. For this reason, rocket and satellite workers are discussing the different international aspects. In order to be prepared for any misunderstandings that may arise among nations, and to boost the peaceful aspects of space flight, the United Nations has been approached.

The world's rocket societies, through their international federation, have been interested in establishing a close contact with UNESCO (United Nations Educational, Scientific and Cultural Organization), because the societies' members feel that the United Nations must assist in supervising the world's attempt to explore and conquer space. Clark M. Eichelberger, executive director of the American Association for the United Nations, has also suggested that the UN take over international supervision of the satellite programs to make certain that interplanetary rivalry between the United States and the Soviet does not "mask military projects of frightful destruction."

Before we launch any satellites, it is wise that we ask whether we shall experience any international conflicts during the initial phase of the satellites' explorations; and whether political confusion in one way or another between two or more nations would result if a satellite went astray.

When dozens of small unmanned satellites are circling the globe in all types of orbits within a few years, the scientific organizations behind them will be interested in world-wide co-operation regarding tracking and exchange of information. Actually, all countries in the world will be involved when circumpolar orbits are used; special tracking vessels will be operating in every ocean. During the IGY we shall experience close international co-operation with respect to tracking; successful achievement of complete scientific studies depend upon this aid. The countries involved, therefore, must agree on the distribution and magnitude of the tracking operations. Many of the territories will be behind iron-curtain or Communist nations. Consequently, West and East must attempt to meet each other on a friendly basis if either is to benefit from satellite science. Since the Soviets are participants in the IGY, we might expect that they will be as interested in international co-operation as we are. This could lead to permanent international harmony in all satellite ventures.

In this case, we visualize that one political difficulty will be avoided: the question of occupying the air space—or just space—over another country's territory. Many experts feel that *space law*—a new form of binding international legal practice and rules—will be required for the peaceful advancement of space flight.

Space law, as applied to satellite science, has been studied thoroughly by the well-known Washington lawyer, Andrew G. Haley, past president of the American Rocket Society. According to his analysis of international law and space flight, it is evident that each and every sovereign nation can demand that no man-made object or vehicle shall pass over such a sovereign's territory without permission of the sovereign—and this has no reference to the height at which the passage is made as long as such a passage might be a means of acquiring intelligence concerning the sovereign or a threat in any manner to the sovereign. Historically the sovereign has always asserted exclusive, absolute dominion over the land and everything incident to the land, including the space above the land.

While we have an almost complete freedom of the seas, there is actually no such thing as freedom of the air. Air travel between any two nations is still entangled in a complex of bilateral and international rules and regulations. In the light of the rules of law and the idea of untrammeled sovereignty, the inauguration of the unmanned Earth satellite programs stands out as perhaps the most felicitous incident of the generation. The entire *Vanguard* program could have been stopped by the protest of a single sovereign nation over which the satellite might pass. The entire program could have been endlessly delayed by making it the subject of detailed international negotiation. "The inauguration of the program in a peaceful and uncomplicated manner is a great achievement of scientists throughout the world," Haley says.

We might also ask if a satellite could in any fashion go astray, and the answer is yes. During launching, a malfunctioning rocket component would be enough to send the vehicle off course. It could happen that it would crash in another country, causing some physical damage. But judging from past airplane incidents—it has happened many times that foreign aircraft have crashed in this country and vice versa—we can find not one case that has resulted in any international political difficulties. The risk and probability for such accidents are mutual, and they are always unintentional. The same view will apply to satellite flight as long as the satellites are not used militarily.

Scientists seem quite confident that complete disintegration or vaporization will kill a satellite spiraling back to Earth. If such vaporization is not complete, however, we might get a fall-out of miniature electronic components scattered over thousands of square miles. Consequently, the chance of finding a satellite component in the back yard is rather remote.

Other important aspects of international co-operation are those connected with telecommunications and meteorology. Communications from or to Earth through space must be by radio. Remote control of an unmanned Earth satellite either from Earth or from some spatial point, and automatic imparting of knowledge through instrumentation in the satellite and on Earth by use of radio are comparatively simple problems.

But the day is not distant when the problems of remote control will multiply tremendously, and with the advent of the manned satellite, the problems of communication will become quite complicated. They will call for more and more use of the radio spectrum. It follows that distribution and use of channels and frequencies must be governed on an international basis. Quite logically, the International Astronautical Federation has already approached the International Telecommunications Union (ITU) for a thorough investigation of the problems expected.

The program submitted to the ITU calls for the ITU's International Radio Consultative Committee to undertake a study of communication requirements for travel in space. It was also requested that the International Frequency Registration Board advise as to the availability of frequencies for such purposes. UNESCO, IAF, and rocket and astronautical organizations throughout the world were requested to co-operate in all phases of the basic study made by the ITU. After such co-operative studies are completed, the ITU will initiate formal steps to effect the allocation of radio frequencies, not only for travel in space but also for communication to and from satellites.

It is well that lawyers and political experts have become interested in satellite science. It is also significant that the international aspects of satellite science are being considered and studied; thus we shall be prepared to meet any difficulties that may arise when satellite traffic becomes heavy.

Our more immediate problems, however, such as how to get the satellites up, are of greater concern right now. We will leave it to the experts to discuss who owns the universe. We want to convince ourselves that our rocket and missile technology really permits us to advance into space.

3. Long-Playing Rockets

Today, the rocket is the only engine that is usable for flights in the very upper layers of the atmosphere or in space, where air-breathing engines are useless. The rocket carries with it the oxygen needed for the combustion of its fuel, and in addition develops the greatest thrust per unit of engine weight with the smallest frontal area per pound of thrust of all propulsion devices. Although we take tremendously powerful rockets for granted, it is necessary to review a bit of rocket technology to understand how it is applied to satellite vehicles. Also, it is important to stress that a vast number of instability factors and difficulties still are encountered in connection with launching and firing large liquid-propellant rockets.

The first V–2 was launched from Peenemünde in the spring of 1942. It rose slowly, gathered momentum and roared into the clouds. Then, suddenly, the motor stopped. The large rocket came tumbling out of the clouds and crashed into the sea with a tremendous explosion. Something had gone wrong, and something went wrong with all except one of the first 8 V–2s fired. A German color movie, released after the war, shows in detail the disastrous effects of one such mishap. The revenge weapon, the 46-foot V–2, is erected on its launching stand with the usual layer of frost covering the skin around the liquid-oxygen tank (temperature of *LOX*, liquid oxygen, is –297 degrees Fahrenheit). The operator pulls the igniter switch and the first stage of the starting is in process: liquid oxygen and alcohol flow by gravity into the motor and burn to produce seven tons of thrust, insufficient to lift the rocket. When the operator is convinced that the burning is normal, and that the flames are licking around the rocket base and launching platform smoothly, he pushes the button for the second firing stage. Inside the rocket, hydrogen peroxide and permanganate are mixed, forming a steam that drives the turbine pumps, which in turn force the fuels into the combustion chamber. The rocket is rising slowly, uncertainly. Standing still for a moment, only a foot above the stand, it tilts over and its nine and one half tons of liquid fuels explode with a tremendous force. A huge ball of fire engulfs the launching site.

Of our own *Viking* rockets, quite similar to the V–2s, only seven out of twelve firings can be said to have been successful. *Viking* Number 6 executed violent maneuvers in flight because the steering fins failed; Number 8 broke loose on a static firing test and destroyed itself; Number 10 did not leave the ground at all, the motor exploding on the first flight attempt.

Every rocket designer and manufacturer will confirm that any high-thrust liquid rocket motor, even of the most advanced design, is likely to hold a few sinister surprises. In the early days of German rocketry, and more recently, at our current testing facilities, all types of accidents have occurred and still occur during testing of engines. The rocket engineer keeps his fingers crossed before every firing, asking himself whether the thing will work—and hoping that it will. Before any *Viking* rocket was launched from the White Sands Proving Ground in New Mexico, the instrumentation, the fuel system and the rocket motor had been tested and retested many times. And still the rocket engineers from the Naval Research Laboratory, which was responsible for the venture, were always uncertain whether the rocket would take off and fly successfully.

Besides being the most efficient propulsion device, the rocket motor is usually considered the simplest of all combustion engines. An aircraft gas turbine contains thousands of precision parts while a liquid rocket is essentially made up of a combustion chamber, two propellant tanks, and a turbine pump system for driving the fuels under pressure into the motor; other than the pumps, there are no moving parts involved. Why is it, then, that so many failures and incidents have been recorded? And since a *Viking*-type rocket is just the type device that will be used for the early satellite vehicles, is it not likely that we are taking quite a chance? Will it work?

When we examine the general characteristics of a rocket of the kind that might be used for putting up a satellite, we soon find that there are quite a few difficulties involved in designing the vehicle, as well as in launching it. Such a rocket represents a most intricate and expensive apparatus.

A perfect rocket flight depends on a great many factors, the two most important being successful operation of the rocket motor and faultless functioning of the automatic stabilization system. Growing out of these requirements are the specifications that electrical and other equipment must operate at pressures ranging from atmospheric to near vacuum. Because the launching velocity of a large rocket is so slow—starting from zero—initial guidance is difficult without the use of a launching tower, or either graphite steering vanes in the exhaust stream or a *gimbaled* motor. This type of power plant is mounted in a swivel structure that permits tilting of the motor in any direction.

Another problem is the fact that portions of the rocket's skin will heat up at supersonic speeds; also, even though a rocket is a one-shot proposition, components must be designed with reliability approaching 100 per cent. So much depends on each element in the chain of events that each must operate successfully.

Rocket flight is not particularly smooth. Equipment, therefore, must not only be self-powered, self-running, and self-controlled, but also must be stable under conditions of high accelerations, vibration, heating and considerable tossing.

Gas temperatures in the rocket motor run from 5,000 to 6,000 degrees Fahrenheit. (A jet aircraft turbine operates at about 1,800 degrees Fahrenheit.) Therefore, the motor must be cooled. In a *regenerating cooling system* the motor parts are cooled by means of a built-in coil in which the propellant is used as the coolant fluid. The heat absorbed by the coolant is therefore not wasted but rather augments the initial energy content of the propellant prior to injection, thereby increasing the exhaust velocity slightly. Without cooling, the wall in the rocket combustion chamber acts as a heat sponge, absorbing heat energy. When the wall temperature approachs the melting point of the wall material, it will be only a matter of seconds before the motor explodes.

An important factor in the stability of rocket combustion is the matter of continuous flow of the propellant and oxidizer. In a large missile, the fuel system involves several valves. Since the temperature of liquid oxygen is –297 degrees Fahrenheit, it is quite possible that some of the valves will stick and shut off the flow. This may result in nothing but motor cutoff, but if fuel alone is allowed to accumulate in the rocket, the situation could easily lead to a catastrophe.

Control of instability in rocket burning is an art that rocket engineers have tried to master. It involves many problems connected with the combustion and flow of gases through the rocket nozzle, fuel pressure, shock waves and other phenomena. These are essential problems that rocket engineers must consider carefully in order to make the large vehicle fly.

Even though supersonic rocket motors are available, it is obvious that they are useless unless they can be used to perform an assigned mission with high accuracy, such as a satellite project requires. In the area of rocket power-plant installations are included such items as fuel systems, lubrication systems, lines, fittings, seals and cooling systems. The most aggravating factor in supersonic flight is the temperature that is encountered. The increase of rocket skin temperature with increasing velocity is considerable, and this increase can critically affect the various systems. At relatively moderate speeds, the usefulness of rubber materials, aluminum and titanium ends. Our earnest hopes are with engineers who work on the development of new materials. These men are trying to solve many rocket problems through the use of superalloys, ceramics and *cermets*, part metal, part nonmetal.

Of paramount importance and a predominant source of concern for the engineer who must consider supersonic installations is the problem of the effects of high-speed flight upon fuel systems. It is estimated that a rocket flying at twice the speed of sound at an altitude of 50,000 feet will lose almost 20 per cent of the propellant as a result of vaporization.

A big problem in stabilizing a rocket arises because the rocket's center of gravity changes as the propellants are burned. Also, it is not easy to guide a rocket remotely, since certain exhaust gases absorb, reflect and diffuse radio waves. This makes it difficult to send information from the missile and send guidance signals to it. At high altitudes the problem is particularly onerous because the exhaust tends to grow bushy or blossom out as atmospheric pressure decreases. If the rocket has no electronic equipment for guidance, it must rely solely upon its built-in equipment for steering.

One would imagine that a rocket aimed straight up would have no difficulty in following a vertical path. But tests have proved differently. We remember that Number 6 *Viking* roared aloft out of control because the steering fins did not function. Many White Sands engineers recall with horror the time that a V-2 screamed into a hillside cemetery at 3,000 miles per hour outside Juárez, Mexico. No international fuss developed, but the incident did point up the initiative of the Mexican townsfolk. Concession stands were established at the site and small boys were peddling pieces of the "missile" as souvenirs. Unwary tourists soon found that their purchases were distressingly similar to odd pieces of wrecked automobiles, easily procurable at any city dump.

It is the external sleekness of a missile that has led to the tacit assumption that there seems to be nothing to the problem of designing and flying large rockets. This idea is understandable, especially in view of the apparent simplicity of the rocket concept. Upon analyzing the stabilization of a large rocket, however, we find that an intricate and expensive system is required. This problem is made more complicated by the variation of missile dynamics during flight. At take-off, the forward velocity is so low that aerodynamic forces are negligible and the rocket behaves as a wingless body would. As the speed increases, aerodynamic forces become significant and the equations of motion of the vehicle become more complicated. Later the lack of air at the upper altitudes reduces these forces until the rocket again behaves as a wingless body.

N. E. Felt, Jr., Martin's operations manager for *Project Vanguard*, says that Martin engineers, when designing the *Viking*, initially proposed that the control forces be obtained by the deflection of vanes placed in the jet stream. The chief advantage of this system was based on the experiences obtained with the V-2. However, the disadvantages of this system became apparent when an investigation of alternate control methods was conducted. When a gimbaled motor system was compared with the jet-vane method, the latter system showed a considerable weight penalty, a difficulty connected with vane durability because of the heat, a reduction of propellant burning-rate due to vane drag in the jet stream, and a high complexity. The gimbaled motor with its swiveling structure appeared to be the better unit.

Deflection of a rocket motor during flight is not a simple task.

The complex steering system consists of electrical and hydraulic components, delicate valves and precision fittings. The most important mechanical unit in a stabilization system is the automatic pilot, whose main component is the *gyroscope*.

The gyroscope has the property, like a child's spinning hoop or top, of always pointing in the same direction. In a satellite-carrying rocket, the gyroscope—mounted in the nose section—points upward. If the rocket tends to depart from the desired line of flight, perhaps because of wind gusts or turbulent air, the gyroscope immediately sends a message to the gimbaled motor, which tilts over slightly to bring the vehicle back on course. The gyroscope remains spinning in the original position of setting, in this case, vertically.

It sounds rather uncomplicated when we say that the gyroscope "sends a message to the gimbaled motor." And it would not be fair to refrain from sketching what takes place during a corrective maneuver. If the rocket attitude differs from the desired flight path, an *error voltage* appears at the output of the vertical gyroscope. The error voltage, a tiny amount of electric current proportional to the off-course angle, is sent to an *amplifier*, a component that builds the current up to a power that through mechanical and hydraulic links is capable of deflecting the gimbaled motor. The amount of deflection is proportional to the error voltage. In its tilted position, the motor begins correcting the rocket's attitude error. When the rocket has returned to its desired attitude, the motor returns to its normal position.

The rocket engines for the early satellites will be similar to the *Viking* rockets but improved in two principal ways. First, the new rockets will be more efficient. Second, the new rockets will have no fins; in this way we can design a vehicle that is completely stabilized by the thrust of its motor. The gimbal mounting usually is designed to permit a tilt of $+5$ degrees from the center line of the vehicle. The gimbal structure was built into the first *Viking*, and into all the subsequent ones, although they also had fins to assist in stabilization.

The finless rocket has been under study for several years and a few small finless rockets have been fired experimentally. The Martin and NRL engineers have performed much analysis that has proved the finless rocket theoretically workable, and they had sufficient confidence in this work to suggest large finless rockets for the first satellite vehicles. Actually, it was known in 1946 that the use of fins for longitudinal rocket stabilization produced unwanted movements and added weight to the rocket's structure. They give no assistance to the rocket's course at the moment of launching, when its forward speed is low, nor near the end of the powered flight, when the rocket is above the Earth's atmosphere.

Having examined some of the more vital aspects of a typical liquid-propellant rocket, we should consider *velocity*. The speed required, after all, is the most essential element in getting a satellite into an orbit.

There are only two ways to achieve the most in velocity for a rocket. We can increase the exhaust velocity of the gases by using more powerful propellants and more efficient rocket motors, because the exhaust speed determines the velocity of the rocket itself. Or we can improve the rocket's *mass ratio* (ratio of the total rocket weight to the weight after fuel is expended) by reducing dead weight to a minimum. As far as improving mass ratio is concerned, tremendous difficulties are involved.

A rocket with a total weight of 272 pounds and a final weight of 100 pounds after all the fuel is consumed would have a mass ratio of 2.72 to 1. It has been calculated that, no matter what type fuel is used, this is the mass ratio needed to drive a rocket at the exhaust velocity of its own fuel. If a rocket with this mass ratio uses liquid hydrogen and liquid oxygen as fuel, the rocket would eventually travel at the exhaust velocity of the fuel, about 12,000 miles per hour.

Assume, however, that we want the rocket to go twice as fast as its exhaust velocity. To attain this speed, the mass ratio is not doubled but squared. The mass ratio required is now 7.4 to 1. If we want to travel at three times the exhaust velocity, the mass ratio (2.72) must now be cubed—which means a mass ratio of about 20 to 1. Such a rocket would have to be 95 per cent fuel and only 5 per cent rocket and pay load. When we get to a mass ratio of this size, the size of the over-all rocket is gigantic.

A new fuel with a higher exhaust velocity than is possible today would of course mean that a much lower mass ratio would be required to get the same final speed. Thousands of propellant combinations have been examined for this purpose. Propellants ranging from aluminum powder to turpentine have been tried. The development of a pure and safe *ozone,* a potential superoxidizer, has been reported. The product might prove to be a major step forward in the development of rocket travel of the future, if the claims for the ozone are true. While one scientist says that for years he thought he had a safe pure form of ozone gas only to have it blow up without any apparent provocation, another scientist predicts that the new liquefied gas may help speed Earth satellites out to the fringe of Earth's gravity.

Gerald W. Platz, head of the ozone technology group at Armour Research Foundation, says that the past history of ozone research has been full of reports about spontaneous, unpredictable explosions. But the ozone developed in purified form at Armour has the characteristics of a safe product.

Ozone has been called supercharged oxygen. It forms naturally in the atmosphere along the path of a lightning bolt, but quickly reverts to stable oxygen. What happens is that the normal molecule of oxygen containing two atoms is broken up by the electrical discharge, forming ozone, which contains three oxygen atoms. The hitchhiking atoms, hungry to get back in their proper places, quickly latch on to other free oxygen atoms to form stable oxygen. In laboratory production, ozone formed by the passage of an electrical discharge through oxygen is trapped to prevent reunion of its extra atom with free oxygen atoms.

A report by Platz and his associate, C. K. Hersh, indicates that ozone is hazardous only when not completely purified. The new processing, they say, makes their ozone "100 per cent pure"; since the ozone is pure, it can be produced and handled without mishap. Such pure ozone has remarkable stability against heat, impact and vibration—all trigger mechanisms blamed for lab-shattering explosions. Stored in specially cleaned containers, the chemical can be dropped from great heights or withstand great vibration forces over a long period of time. This development is significant; it is just what the rocket propellant experts have been looking for. We are also waiting for certain *exotic* propellants, powerful nonhydrocarbon fuels with high exhaust velocities. These fuels and certain superoxidizers are currently being tested in our laboratories. In the meantime, however, we shall be confined to the use of the more proven and conservative propellants.

A powerful rocket propellant is the combination of liquid oxygen and liquid hydrogen. However, this is also the most dangerous and difficult combination to handle. Liquid oxygen at a temperature of −297 degrees Fahrenheit, is cheap to produce and is abundant. It can be handled safely when stored in vented and well-insulated containers. Liquid hydrogen, on the other hand, has a temperature of −423 degrees Fahrenheit, which presents extremely difficult storage and handling problems. A rocket with liquid-oxygen liquid-hydrogen propellants would require very large and well-insulated tanks and comprise an extremely hazardous vehicle even when not in use. Dr. Dornberger says he would want to stand several miles from a launching site if someone were to attempt the fueling of a rocket with liquid hydrogen and liquid oxygen.

The most widely used rocket fuel at the moment is liquid oxygen and alcohol, which produces fairly high thrusts and exhaust velocities. The performance of this propellant combination is considerably lower than that of the liquid hydrogen–oxygen combination but the alcohol is simple to store and handle and presents no special hazards that ordinary care will not accommodate. Some of the early satellite rocket propellants will be a combination of about 95 per cent gasoline, 4 per cent alcohol and one per cent silicone oil, which will act as a flow coolant. Liquid oxygen will be used as the oxidizer.

The more practical problems of propellant selection include low price, abundance of raw materials, availability, stability in storage, high density, ease of handling, nontoxicity and convenient freezing and boiling points. These factors exert a more powerful influence on propellant selection, particularly for military field operations, than does propellant performance alone.

There are several schools of thought as to how a satellite can be placed in its orbit. Writing in a semimonthly Moscow journal, Professor Kirill Stanyukovich, of the USSR Academy of Science Commission for Inter-Planetary Communication, recently reported that Soviet engineers "believe it is possible to build larger satellites than those now being discussed in the Western press." His article in the political journal, the *News*, said that the present level of automatic and remote-control engineering makes entirely practical the idea of a composite-stage rocket that can climb to a height of 250 miles, come to a stop at its maximum altitude and, at this precise moment,

explode from its side an 18-inch-diameter satellite having an initial
velocity of about five miles per second.

The Soviet doctor of technical sciences observed that such a satellite can be given an initial speed of 18,000 miles per hour in two
ways: "A three-stage rocket, the satellite being the third stage, could
be constructed. But this is extremely complicated. The simpler way
is to shoot out the cosmic ball with an explosion that will at the
same time break up the remainder of the rocket. Calculations show
that in order to obtain such a speed with the use of the powerful
explosives TNT or hexogen, the explosive force has to be 10 times
the weight of the body to be ejected. It is, of course, difficult to say
now which method scientists in different countries will choose. Both
methods, it seems to me, are valid."

In this country, three different launching methods have been discussed and they will probably all be tried within the next few years.

Professor P. E. Sandorff of Massachusetts Institute of Technology, five weeks prior to President Eisenhower's announcement of the
Vanguard project, offered interesting details of what he termed the
airplane-launching method. Sandorff considers the possibility of
launching a satellite vehicle with a 500-pound pay load from an aircraft (such as the B–52) at 9.5 miles' altitude. In this way, by lifting
the vehicle through much of the atmosphere and adding the aircraft's speed to the vehicle, a satellite could be launched with a
lower weight and cost than would be the case for a ground-launched
vehicle. Sandorff shows that a two-stage rocket weighing 100,000
pounds with 200 pounds' pay load could achieve a 200-mile altitude
orbit. In comparison, a three-stage-rocket vehicle launched from the
ground would weigh about 250,000 pounds with a corresponding increase in cost.

A significant advantage of the airplane-step arrangement is the
improved reliability of the entire system, according to Sandorff.
Rocket-powered space vehicles, being new and highly automatized
instruments, do not yet compare in dependability with aircraft. The
separation of two stages is an operation involving considerable difficulty. The rocket-powered lower step would probably contain several motors and consequently show a higher probability of malfunc-
tion. Sandorff thinks that the chance for success for a three-stage
rocket is about one in three while for a two-stage rocket using the
airplane step the chances for success are about two in three. A pro-

gram to put 10 satellites into orbit would cost $170 million if the larger, all-rocket design were used, while if the airplane step were adopted, the cost would be $48 million plus the cost of airplane modification, operation and attrition.

Significant advances are being made in the efficiency of air-breathing engines, as evidenced by the advent of purely thrust-borne aircraft in the past few years. Aerodynamics has kept pace with airplanes designed for 1,100 miles per hour at 7.5 miles' altitude. If these trends continue, Sandorff visualizes an airplane step that will launch the rocket at 7.5 or 9.5 miles' altitude at an initial speed of perhaps 3,000 miles per hour. The aircraft in combination with its load might have the external appearance of the Douglas X–3 *Stiletto* research airplane. The power loading would be relatively high, so that take-off would be an easy operation, but the climb to the service ceiling of the aircraft—10 or 11 miles' altitude—would still take perhaps an hour. A straight launching run then would be made, with full engine power, employing afterburners and auxiliary ram-jets mounted in the wings. The sonic barrier would be passed quickly, but it would take half an hour to reach full speed. Meanwhile the airplane would dive to the lowest permissible altitude for rocket efficiency, which would also be the optimum design performance altitude for the airplane. Here, at top speed, a pull-up maneuver would be made to place the rocket into the optimum flight path. JATO rockets might be used for an additional boost. The cargo would be dropped, it would fall away 50 to 100 feet, until its rocket engines developed full thrust, at which time the rocket vehicle would accelerate swiftly ahead.

"If such designs materialize it seems unlikely that space vehicles will ever take off from the Earth's surface under rocket power," Sandorff says. It is likely that the concept will be tried in the future. With tomorrow's B–58 supersonic delta-wing bombers, it might be possible to launch a satellite rocket from approximately 13 miles' altitude.

The second launching concept, the *balloon-launching* method, has intrigued the U. S. Air Force. Even though the Air Force has a five-year satellite project under way, small balloon-launched vehicles might be built first.

The man behind the balloon method is Kurt R. Stehling, formerly with Bell Aircraft, now in charge of power-plant development for *Project Vanguard*. The idea actually has been tried with a small solid-propellant rocket, the *Deacon*, by Dr. James A. Van Allen of the University of Iowa's Department of Physics, under an ONR contract. While the *Deacon* was not an orbital vehicle, Van Allen was able to explore altitudes up to 65 miles with very inexpensive equipment—balloon and vehicle cost about $2,000.

Because a large liquid-propellant-powered vehicle would be costly and difficult to build, Stehling, in collaboration with R. M. Missert, of the University of Iowa's Department of Physics, has concentrated on the possibility of launching a small orbital vehicle from a high altitude. In an *Aviation Age* article Stehling writes that his minimum vehicle could be the forerunner of larger and more complicated ones. It could obtain information on ballistic flight paths, supersonic high-altitude aerodynamic drag, guidance and radio propagation.

The success of the *Deacon* project led to Stehling's consideration of a larger vehicle (30-pound pay load) launched from a balloon at near-drag-free conditions and capable of an orbital flight path at an altitude of 150 miles or more. He says the main features of the vehicle, which he calls *Saloon*, are low total weight, and simple construction with a minimum number of parts that could fail—necessary because launching takes place away from human control. The rocket may be designed without streamlining because of the low drag involved when launching from great altitudes. This means that standard, nonstreamlined power-booster rockets are immediately possible.

Stehling also stresses the use of high acceleration rates and relatively short burning times. These were deliberately chosen so that less power would be required to lift the rocket plus its propellant load against gravity. Reasonable mass ratios and thrust-weight ratios are also possible. These were chosen to permit the application of techniques that are available now or will soon be developed, rather than of hypothetical future ones. Only 50 pounds of controls are built into the second stage to permit small adjustments of the ballistic flight path during the powered phase. The third stage is assumed to be able to reach an elliptical orbit without further guidance.

The 50 pounds of controls will include a timer or a chamber pressure sensor to actuate the third-stage blowoff device at the moment the second-stage rocket reaches the *burn-out* point, the moment when all propellants are consumed.

A thrust-weight ratio of 3 has been chosen by Stehling to give a firing period long enough to permit application of some control, if needed.

The third stage is the orbital vehicle, the actual satellite. It is fired at the moment of second-stage burnout. No control is provided since the second stage is expected to have entered the free-fall or orbital path. The third stage will enter an elliptical orbit. The 30-pound pay load is equal in weight to that of the *Deacon* vehicle and somewhat more than the weight of the *Vanguard* satellite.

The advantages of the balloon-launched satellite vehicle include low cost and simple construction, which is made possible because of the reduction of aerodynamic drag. This is due to launching the vehicle from higher altitude. An upper limit of 21 miles has been mentioned as the launching altitude; this would require a balloon with a capacity of six million cubic feet. A minimum of complex hardware is required, and the pay load is high enough to get a useful minimum satellite into an orbit. The proposed vehicle is a possibility for the near, rather than the distant, future.

The third launching concept, of course, is the method that will be used for the *Vanguard* satellites, often referred to as LPR, or *Long-Playing Rockets*. The basketball satellites will be brought up to their proposed orbits between 200 and 800 miles above the Earth by multistage rockets launched vertically.

When we build a rocket capable of carrying a certain pay load, and make that pay load another rocket carrying the same percentage of propellants, when the smaller vehicle has burned its propellants it will have achieved twice the speed that either rocket could attain by itself. A three-step rocket will do even better; a rocket vehicle consisting of a sufficient number of steps could literally reach any desired terminal speed. This is the reason that an improvement in rocket propellants is not of paramount importance for the successful launching of a small satellite. In the case of the *Vanguard* vehicle, a three-step configuration will be sufficient, the first finless stage carrying the other two rockets and the satellite as its pay load, the second stage carrying the third rocket and the satellite, and the last one carrying only the satellite.

The main-stage engine will be more efficient than the *Viking* en-

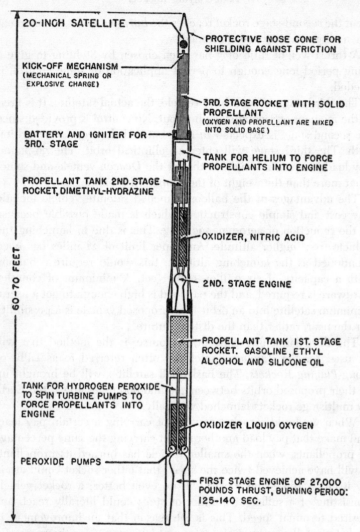

Schematic view of propulsion system in a three-stage satellite vehicle of the *Vanguard* type. No gyromechanisms or stabilization components are shown. The propellants used for the second stage are *hypergolic*, that is, oxidizer and fuel ignite upon contact, no battery or ignition system being required.

gine, and therefore more powerful. It will have a thrust of 27,000 pounds at sea level (about the same as three jet engines) and an operating time of 131 seconds. Built by the General Electric Company, the engine consists of a regeneratively cooled thrust chamber, a gimbaled mounting, propellant valves, turbopump and high-pressure lines. Liquid oxygen and a mixture of gasoline, ethyl alcohol, and silicone oil will be forced into the thrust chamber by turbine-driven pumps. The turbine will be powered by the decomposition products of hydrogen peroxide. In this type turbine, liquid peroxide is converted in a steam generator into hot steam, which is forced against the turbine blades, thereby driving the pump.

The second-stage rocket, as well as the first-stage, will be finless. The subcontract for construction of the second stage was awarded to the Aerojet-General Corporation. This power plant will also consist of a regeneratively cooled thrust chamber mounted in a gimbal. Nitric acid, which contains quite a bit of oxygen, will be the oxidizer and unsymmetrical dimethyl-hydrazine the fuel. Flow of these propellants to the thrust chamber will be effected by helium pressurization of the propellant tanks, rather than by a steam turbine, as in the first-stage motor.

The third stage of the *Vanguard* rocket will be powered by a solid-propellant motor, and will consist of the motor, a structure for attaching it to the second stage and for imparting spin to the third stage, and the satellite package and mounting structure. Builders of the third-stage rocket are the Grand Central Rocket Company and the Allegany Ballistics Laboratory. The whole *Vanguard* configuration is close to 70 feet high.

With a main-stage thrust of 27,000 pounds, we get the following approximate weight specifications for a *Vanguard* satellite vehicle:

Satellite (including nose cone)	30 pounds
Third-Stage Structure	60 pounds
Empty Weight	90 pounds
Gross Weight	270 pounds
Second-Stage Structure	540 pounds
Empty Weight	810 pounds
Gross Weight	2,430 pounds
First-Stage Structure	4,860 pounds
Empty Weight	7,290 pounds
Gross Weight	21,870 pounds

While these figures should not be taken as exact, they probably will not differ much from the actual ones. The total gross weight of 21,870 pounds represents about the same weight as that of a *Sabrejet* fighter.

Dr. Martin Summerfield, professor at Princeton University, has revealed some specifications for a three-stage rocket required to put a *Vanguard*-type satellite into an orbit as far as 400 miles above the Earth. His calculations are based on the performance that might be achieved by each stage of the satellite rocket and on the characteristics of the *Viking* Number 11 rocket plus expected advances in the state of the art since this rocket was designed by Martin in 1951. His specifications included the following data:

	1st Stage	2d Stage	3d Stage
Gross Mass	15,000 pounds	2,000 pounds	200 pounds
Thrust	38,000 pounds	8,400 pounds	730 pounds
Burning Time	70 seconds	50 seconds	50 seconds
Structure Mass	1,800 pounds	300 pounds	30 pounds
Ratio of Structure to Gross Mass	12 per cent	15 per cent	15 per cent
Pay Load	2,000 pounds	200 pounds	30 pounds
Total Velocity at Burnout	5,200 miles per hour	12,500 miles per hour	19,500 miles per hour

Dr. Summerfield is counting on a first-stage thrust of 38,000 pounds for this operation, while the actual *Vanguard* rocket will have a thrust of only 27,000 pounds. Regardless of the satellite pay load, it is obvious that more thrust is needed to bring the satellite up to more distant orbits: a satellite destined for a 500-mile orbit needs a greater initial push than if the orbit were to be 250 miles, even though the orbital velocity is less at 500 miles.

If the satellite package were to be the nose of the vehicle, it could become too hot, probably in excess of 1,000 degrees Fahrenheit. One alternative would be to build the satellite with a heavy skin and insulation, which would incidentally present a problem of excess weight. Another alternative would be to shelter the satellite with a conical, disposable nose for the third-stage rocket. Since the heating would occur during the last part of the first-stage flight and the first part of the second-stage flight, that is, after high speed has been

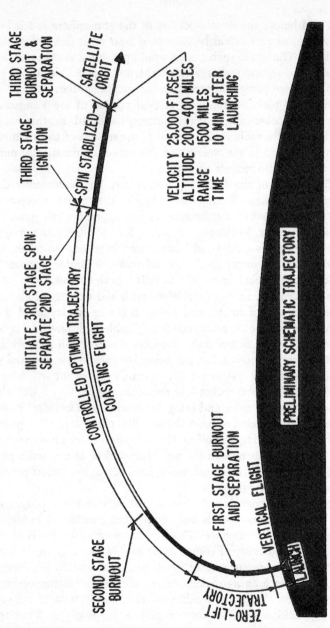

THIRD STAGE
BURNOUT &
SEPARATION

SATELLITE
ORBIT

THIRD STAGE
IGNITION

SPIN STABILIZED

INITIATE 3RD STAGE SPIN:
SEPARATE 2ND STAGE

VELOCITY   25,000 FT/SEC
ALTITUDE   200-400 MILES
RANGE   1500 MILES
TIME   10 MIN. AFTER
            LAUNCHING

CONTROLLED OPTIMUM TRAJECTORY
COASTING FLIGHT

SECOND STAGE
BURNOUT

FIRST STAGE BURNOUT
AND SEPARATION

VERTICAL FLIGHT

ZERO-LIFT
TRAJECTORY

LAUNCH

PRELIMINARY SCHEMATIC TRAJECTORY

View of the *Vanguard* launching technique and trajectory. A spin of the third-stage rocket (and satellite) is initiated to obtain greater stabilization. (Official U.S. Navy Photo)

reached and before the denser portion of the atmosphere is left behind, the conical nose could be jettisoned near or at the end of the
second stage. The use of such a cone would provide a weight penalty
for the first and second stages of the flight, and this penalty is one of
the many that are being considered in the weight studies.

The first-step rocket is the most critical portion of the *Vanguard*
vehicle; if this rocket fails, the entire attempt will fail. Furthermore,
the guidance of the main rocket is vital to the success of the venture,
since any deviation in the steering of this rocket automatically puts
the second and third rockets off course.

The flight path of the first-stage rocket may be conveniently divided into three phases. During the first phase the engine accelerates
the rocket vertically to a maximum speed of approximately 3,000 to
4,000 miles per hour. In the second phase, the rocket coasts through
the upper atmosphere. At an altitude between 30 and 40 miles, in
the third phase, the motor in the second rocket is started automatically and the first rocket drops off and falls into the ocean.

The second rocket, having been given an initial velocity of almost
six times the speed of sound, and flying in the upper layers of the
atmosphere where the air resistance is negligible, will have a simple
task compared to the first rocket. The second rocket will soon fly at
a velocity close to 11,000 miles per hour. Its path will curve somewhat, its gyro control system being set so that this event will occur
automatically. The third rocket will then take over from an altitude
of approximately 300 miles and bring the satellite out to its orbit. At
this time, the third rocket releases the satellite, either through a powerful mechanical spring kickoff or through the use of an explosive
charge; the velocity is now in the neighborhood of 18,000 miles per
hour. At the same time, the third rocket has been flying almost parallel to the Earth's curvature.

As we see, the attainment of an orbit just outside the atmosphere
is really not an insurmountable task, even when considered in terms
of present rocket performance. The development costs involved in
the *Vanguard* project are of course considerable, but a great deal of
this money will represent capital investment and various nonrecur-
ring expenses. As long as rockets of present-day performance can
form the basis for designing satellite vehicles, and in view of the estimated $35 million allocated for the project, we might well see 15
satellites being built for use during the IGY. Some of them might

go astray, but we are convinced that most of the satellites ("birds," to their designers) will reach their orbits successfully. The velocity will be fast enough for the satellite to circle the Earth in about 90 minutes; the altitude may be anywhere between 200 and 800 miles. This will be too low for escape into outer space. Gravity and drag will finally have their effects. The satellite will descend in a shallow spiral. After some days, or, if we are lucky, weeks, the satellite will crash into the heavier atmosphere and quickly disintegrate.

4.   What Is Space?

Go up a few miles and life as we know it ends. There, we would no longer have an atmospheric blanket to protect us. High temperatures exist but would not be sensed. X rays and cosmic rays would penetrate our bodies and dissociate our cells. The air pressure would decrease below our blood pressure until our bodily liquids began to boil. Time is always a relative concept. Skyward all is darkness.

At sea level, the molecules comprising air are packed tight together. In every cubic inch there are about 400 quintillion particles. A molecule can barely move without colliding with another one, and its obstacle-free path is only one millionth of an inch.

Because the air at sea level is so dense, scientists at one time believed that nature abhorred a vacuum. Yet we need rise only 70 miles to see that nature prefers a vacuum, for at this altitude, the obstacle-free path of a molecule is 51 inches. The higher the altitude, the farther a molecule can travel before meeting another. At 250 miles' altitude the free path is 43 miles.

In outer space there are about 16 particles per cubic inch, and they hardly ever collide. They exist in a vacuum far less dense than the best we can get in our laboratories, which is thought good at five billion molecules per cubic inch. The free path of particles in space is not known, but is judged to be enormous.

It is interesting to learn how much matter there is in a given volume of outer space. For a volume as large as that of Earth, there is about a quarter of an ounce of meteors and two to three ounces of hydrogen. These figures give an idea of what emptiness is. Connected with this emptiness are unfamiliar concepts of temperature and heat. At 600 miles' altitude, the temperature is about 1,200 degrees Fahrenheit—the melting point of aluminum. Yet aluminum would not melt at that height because there is temperature without heat.

Temperature, as we are most familiar with it, is measured with a thermometer. If we wish to know the temperature of a room, then for ordinary accuracy it does not matter where we mount the thermometer. Its bulb is constantly being bombarded by molecules, which carry energy to the instrument. The liquid level rises or falls depending upon the speed of the molecules. They are in constant motion, with the temperature being highest when their speed is highest. Temperature is simply the measure of molecular speed.

At sea level the molecules are so closely packed together that they no sooner get up speed than they lose it in collisions. But in space, where particles probably travel for millions of miles before they are stopped, they can move at tremendous speeds. The temperature of these particles can reach 10,000 degrees Kelvin and even higher.

The temperature scale using degrees *Kelvin* is based on the point at which a body is entirely devoid of heat and molecular motion ceases; this is marked *zero degrees Kelvin,* or absolute zero. At 273 degrees Kelvin, water freezes; at 373 degrees, water boils. This makes one degree Kelvin equivalent to one degree Centigrade.

The story is told of a young journalist who had read that in space the temperature is several thousand degrees Kelvin. Using this fact as a lead, he wrote a sensational article describing the belt of fire that was surrounding Earth. An instructive experiment for the journalist would have been one in which he was surrounded by interstellar hydrogen traveling at a speed corresponding to 10,000 degrees Kelvin. He would have quickly discovered the difference between temperature and heat. Though each hydrogen particle possesses a tremendously high temperature, it takes a vast volume of them to furnish enough heat to boil a thimbleful of water.

One should not get the impression that a body set in space would immediately freeze. The Earth, for example, is kept warm by its atmosphere, which is heated by the Sun's rays or radiant energy; these rays travel much like light, whose presence is known only when reflected or absorbed by a body. Thus the Sun's heat is not felt until it passes through space and becomes absorbed by our atmosphere and planet. When any body in space intercepts the Sun's rays, then

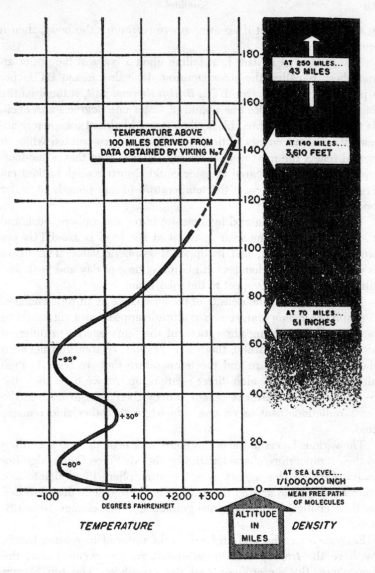

TEMPERATURE ABOVE
100 MILES DERIVED FROM
DATA OBTAINED BY VIKING No.7

AT 250 MILES...
43 MILES

AT 140 MILES...
3,610 FEET

AT 70 MILES...
51 INCHES

AT SEA LEVEL...
1/1,000,000 INCH
MEAN FREE PATH
OF MOLECULES

-100   0   +100   +200   +300
DEGREES FAHRENHEIT

TEMPERATURE

ALTITUDE
IN
MILES

DENSITY

At sea level, the air molecules are packed closely together. In space, they travel many miles before colliding,
and being slowed down. As a result, the temperature of a
molecule, which is a measure of its velocity, is high in outer
space. (Martin, Baltimore)

it too is warmed—but if no atmosphere surrounds the body, then it quickly loses heat.

The amount of radiant heat falling upon a body in the upper atmosphere is called the *solar constant*. Its value is 440 BTUs per square foot per hour. One BTU, *British thermal unit,* is the quantity of heat needed to raise one pound of water one degree Fahrenheit. If the body were painted black, then it would almost completely absorb the radiant energy hitting it, while if it were painted white, it would reflect the most radiant energy. We see then that a one-foot-square black body located in space could absorb enough radiant energy in one hour to raise the temperature of 440 pounds of water one degree Fahrenheit.

Because of losses caused by moisture in the atmosphere, dust, and the air mass itself, the solar constant at sea level is 220 BTUs per square foot per hour, half its upper-atmospheric value. This figure is quite variable: it changes with latitude, time of day and year, and tilt of the body with respect to the solar beam.

The temperature and density of the air change as altitude changes. A graph of air temperature versus altitude appears as a zigzag curve because of the varying absorptions of the Sun's energy in different air layers. At low altitude, there is a "normal" relationship between the actual temperature and the temperature that we feel. At high altitudes, there is no such direct relationship. As we have seen, the few air molecules present cannot convey their heat to us, and the Sun's radiations heat us on one side while the other side remains cold.

The various layers in the atmosphere have been defined according to their temperature characteristics by the Air Force Cambridge Research Center. This agency sees the atmosphere divided into five concentric spheres around the Earth. These are chiefly distinguished by their changes in temperature gradients, which change with altitude.

Each shell has the suffix *sphere*. In the order of increasing height we have the *troposphere*, the *stratosphere*, the *chemosphere*, the *ionosphere*, the *mesosphere*, and the *exosphere*. The top of any sphere is given the suffix *pause*. The upper boundary of the troposphere is called the *tropopause;* of the stratosphere, the *stratopause,* and so forth.

Actually, at no altitude does the temperature gradient change suddenly. If one wishes to mark the spheres according to temperature gradients, then the bounding surfaces or pauses must be allowed to have considerable thickness. At some latitudes, the defining temperature gradient occasionally does not exist, which leads to the elimination of the corresponding sphere.

Our weather is generated in the lowest layer, or troposphere, which is about seven miles high—a mile higher than Mount Everest but equal in height to the mushroom-shaped cloud resulting from an atomic explosion. The troposphere is in thermal equilibrium with the stratosphere above it and the Earth below. When the troposphere absorbs more heat than it reflects, it uses this excess to warm and mix itself. This gives rise to the winds, rains, and displays of summer lightning.

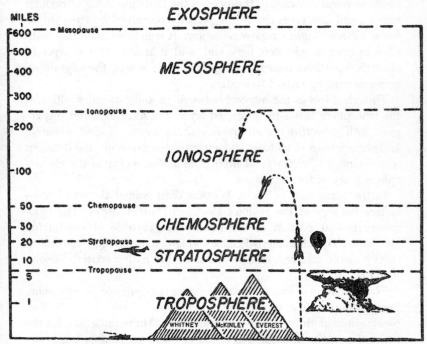

The Earth's atmosphere may be separated into shells, with each layer between shells having unique temperature gradients and physical characteristics. (*Jet Propulsion*)

Man has already flown in the stratosphere, the second atmospheric layer above Earth. In its record-breaking flight, the Douglas *Skyrocket* climbed to about 16 miles' altitude, only 4 miles below the stratopause. High-altitude balloons have traveled through the stratosphere into the next layer. Strong air currents of high velocity, the newly discovered jet streams, are found in the lowest portion of the stratosphere. Here also are the delicate and threadlike cirrus clouds. The air in the stratosphere is clear but turbulent. Occasionally, rare nacreous (mother-of-pearl) clouds are seen, their origin and composition still wrapped in mystery. Streaking across the stratosphere are the ends of meteor trails bright enough to mark the sky even in the daytime.

Above the stratosphere is the chemosphere, which acts like a huge photochemical laboratory. It processes the Sun's incoming ultraviolet energy, and also gives rise to the recently perceived enormously intense, infrared night air-glow radiations. It is in this region that ordinary meteors reach their fiery end, and it is here that a layer of electrified particles sometimes captures radio waves, the capture on occasion causing radio blackouts.

Though it lies in the interval between 50 and 250 miles' altitude, the ionosphere is our most probed layer. We have explored this region with powerful high-frequency radio waves. Rocket research, and observations of meteors and auroras have given us vital data. An instrumented *Wac Corporal* fired from a V–2 rocket in the chemosphere reached the ionopause.

In the early days of radio, Watson Watt coined the word *ionosphere* because of the region's electrical characteristics. The ionosphere is that portion of our atmosphere capable of conducting electricity. This characteristic makes long-distance radio communications possible, and accounts for the small but daily variation in compass readings.

The formation of ions in the atmosphere is a dynamic phenomenon. During the daytime, ultraviolet radiation and X rays from the Sun constantly pass through our upper altitudes. These radiations hit the molecules in the atmosphere, which are tiny and numerous, sometimes sufficiently hard to break them down into atoms. When this occurs, one atom is apt to steal an electron from its former companion. Sometimes, just an electron is knocked loose. In either case, free electrons and atoms with too few or too many electrons are formed.

Such atoms are called *ions*, and the process of making them is called *ionization*.

The particles have two quite important properties: first, unlike neutral particles, they generate an electromagnetic field about themselves, and second, when they form in layers as they do in the ionosphere, the free electrons act as mirrors and reflect certain types of radio waves.

It was through its electromagnetic characteristic and electrical conductivity that the ionosphere was first hypothesized. About 75 years ago, the Scottish physicist Balfour Stewart made an important but then unnoticed contribution to science. He knew that there were daily variations in the strength and direction of the Earth's magnetic field. He also knew that a magnetic field is distorted when an electrical current passes over it. He concluded that there must be a layer someplace in the atmosphere that is conducting electricity.

Not until the beginning of this century was Stewart's theory revived. Physicists agreed that radio waves travel in straight lines much like light. Today, this phenomenon explains our receiving FM and TV broadcasts only within a radius of 25 to 30 miles the sending station, unless repeaters are used. But, the physicists asked, if radio waves travel along line-of-sight paths, how is it that we can receive broadcasts from across the Atlantic Ocean? It was necessary to rehypothesize the ionosphere, an atmospheric region that conducts and reflects electrical waves.

Experimental proof was given in 1924. Short-pulsed radio waves that had been sent straight up into the atmosphere had returned microseconds later. This experiment not only proved that the ionosphere is real but also indicated its height—from the time delay of the radio waves traveling at the speed of light.

Today it is known that the ionosphere extends from an altitude of 50 miles to 250 miles, that it is made up of many horizontal layers, and that each layer contains a seething ocean of electrons easily churned by solar activity, cosmic rays, meteors, and gravitational tugs of the Moon and Sun. Even the time of day, the season, and the year have major effects in this region.

What counts most in the ionosphere is the electron density, normally measured in number of electrons per cubic inch. The higher the density, the more effectively a layer of electrons reflects radio waves. It is natural to characterize each layer with respect to its

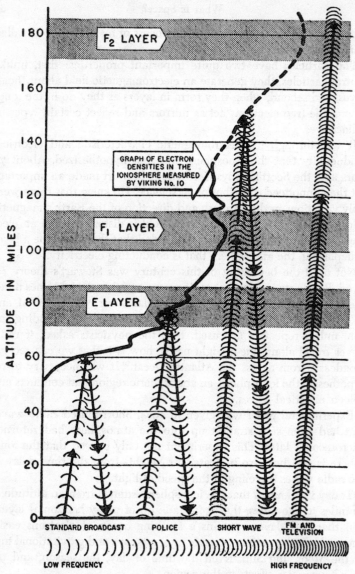

F₂ LAYER

GRAPH OF ELECTRON
DENSITIES IN THE
IONOSPHERE MEASURED
BY VIKING No. 10

F₁ LAYER

E LAYER

ALTITUDE IN MILES

180
160
140
120
100
80
60
40
20
0

STANDARD BROADCAST   POLICE   SHORT WAVE   FM AND TELEVISION

LOW FREQUENCY   HIGH FREQUENCY

Different layers in the ionosphere reflect different type
radio waves. The low frequency or standard broadcast waves
are sent back to Earth from a layer low in the atmosphere,
while high-frequency programs such as FM and TV pass
easily into outer space. (Martin, Baltimore)

electron density. This has been done, the chief layers being named
D, E, and *F.*

The layers have thickness, and vary in the type radio wave they
will reflect. The D layer, which is the lowest one and has the lowest
electron density, reflects long waves such as the standard-broadcast
ones but allows the shorter waves to go by.

A useful analogy is to look at the three layers as sieves, the grid
size of each being proportional to the electron density of each. In
this view, the D layer has the coarsest grid; above it lies the E layer
with a less coarse grid; and finally we have the F layer with the
least coarse grid.

The long waves of the standard-broadcast band being blocked by
the D grid are reflected back to Earth. The shorter waves of the
police-broadcast band stream through the D grid but are stopped
and reflected by the E one. Short-wave broadcasts pass through the
D and E grids to be reflected by the F grid. FM and television signals being shortest of all, scurry through all three grids to provide
entertainment for inhabitants of artificial satellites and other planets.

The E and F layers sometimes each split into two layers; then
subscripts are given to the letter names and the split layers are called
E_1, E_2, and F_1, F_2. It is not yet known why these splits occur.

Having gone this far into the mechanics of the ionosphere, and
seen its apparent simplicity, we can appreciate the time and work
scientists have put into its study. Their theories have received convincing experimental confirmation. Radio probes have shown the existence and heights of the various electron layers. Spectroscopic
studies have proved that speeding atomic particles (corpuscles)
leave the Sun at times of solar flares and bombard our atmosphere,
causing variations in the layers of the ionosphere. Recently, rocket
probes of the ionosphere have confirmed the existence of ultraviolet
radiations and X rays in this region.

It would be fine if the ionosphere behaved in a consistent fashion,
for then we could soon wrap up the problem for all time and move
on to the next. But superimposed on the general pattern are varying
ones. These change from day to day, even from minute to minute.
For example, during a solar fire, when ultraviolet and X-ray radiations are at their highest, the D layer gets a sudden increase in ionized atoms. These, unlike electrons, absorb short waves, and we

experience several hours of radio fading and blackouts, the length and severity depending on the nature of the solar flare.

Sometimes sporadic clouds of electrons hover in the E layer. Why, we do not know. Suddenly, waves that ordinarily would pass right out of the atmosphere are reflected, and we begin receiving FM and TV programs from great distances, programs that should have been cut off at the sending station's line of sight.

Between the ionosphere and the exosphere, which is the outermost atmospheric layer, lies the mesosphere. No man-made vehicle has yet explored this space which stretches from 250 to 600 miles' altitude. Even its temperature gradient is not known, though the region is believed to be one of high but decreasing temperature. Because it experiences the Sun's radiations before the ionosphere does, the mesosphere is probably proportionately more highly ionized, yet since its air density is so much lower, its electron density must also be quite low. Having so few electrons, the mesosphere's influence on radio communications is considered negligible.

At the exosphere we stand on the fringe of outer space. Low in this region some of the neutral atoms and molecules speeding upward never experience a collision, thereby escaping from Earth. This level is called the *critical level* and is believed to be at about 625 miles' altitude. The smaller and faster particles such as hydrogen and helium have lower critical levels, while the heavier particles such as nitrogen have higher ones. Quite gradually, the exosphere diffuses into interplanetary space.

Fortunately for us, from the surface of the Earth it is not possible to see all the sunlight—even with instruments. Most of it is absorbed by our atmosphere. In this way, the atmosphere shields us from the Sun's more intense radiations. As we rise in the atmosphere we perceive strongly the infrared rays at 25 miles' altitude, and then the ultraviolet at 70 miles. Instruments must be used to recognize these radiations because none of our senses can. Biologically we have no need for this ability because none of the ultraviolet and only a minute fraction of the infrared ever reach the Earth.

Violet light is the lower limit of visibility, with a wave length of about 3,850 Ångstrom units. (The Ångstrom unit is a convenient length measure, particularly in the atomic field. The diameter of an atom of hydrogen, for example, is about one Ångstrom unit or

0.00000001 centimeters.) (*See illustration facing page 96.*) Nevertheless, we can easily prove the existence of light below this lower limit. Ordinary photographic paper responds quite readily to exposure to ultraviolet. Instruments show the existence of ultraviolet in the electric arcs thrown by welding rods and arc lights.

The concept of infrared light is quite familiar to us. It is by this light that we take pictures in the "dark." Also, by this light "infrared broilers" cook our food. We can appreciate the existence of these radiations, particularly when they emanate from hot bodies, yet we cannot see them. Neither can we feel the entire band of infrared, which stretches from the normal upper limit of visible light (7,600 Ångstrom units) to the region of high-frequency radio waves.

The rays emitted by the Sun are not bounded by the short ultraviolet waves nor by the long infrared ones. There are ones far shorter and far longer. Above the infrared is the wide band of radio waves extending from radar to the standard-broadcast waves. On the other side, below the short-waved ultraviolet, are the X rays and gamma rays. All these radiations are cut of similar cloth: they travel with the speed of light, are electromagnetic phenomena, and have characteristic wave lengths.

Back in 1900 when research in physics was being done in earthbound laboratories, British and German scientists noted a strange occurrence: the charge in an *electroscope* leaked away no matter how well it was shielded and insulated. (An electroscope is simply a metal cylinder containing a conducting rod. At one end, the rod is insulated from the cylinder, at its other end, the rod holds two thin gold leaves. When the cylinder is given an electrical charge relative to the rod, the leaves spread apart; when the cylinder and rod have the same charge, the leaves hang freely.)

To explain the mysterious leaking, scientists said that somehow the Earth emitted radioactive rays that were neutralizing the charged electroscope. This theory was proved wrong in 1910 when a scientist took some electroscopes up to altitude in balloons; he found that rather than the leakage decreasing, it increased. Later it was observed that the loss reached a peak at 17 miles' altitude, and then slowly lessened. (Recent rocket studies indicate that the leakage becomes constant at 35 miles' altitude.) It was realized that the Earth

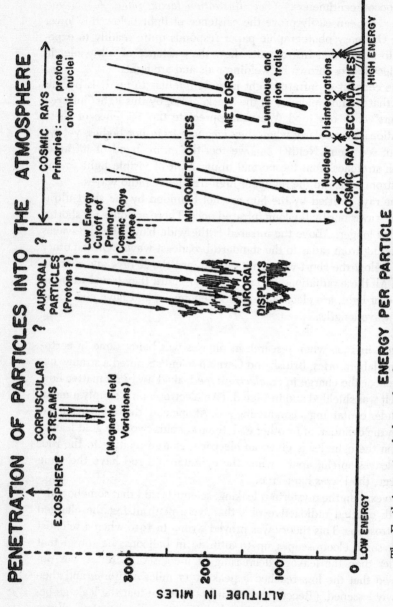

PENETRATION OF PARTICLES INTO THE ATMOSPHERE

EXOSPHERE

CORPUSCULAR STREAMS

AURORAL PARTICLES (Protons?)

(Magnetic Field Variations)

Low Energy Cutoff of Primary Cosmic Rays (kmee)

COSMIC RAYS
Primaries: — protons
— atomic nuclei

MICROMETEORITES

METEORS

Luminous and ion trails

Nuclear Disintegrations

COSMIC RAY SECONDARIES

AURORAL DISPLAYS

ALTITUDE IN MILES

300

200

100

0

LOW ENERGY   ENERGY PER PARTICLE   HIGH ENERGY

The Earth is constantly being bombarded by particles and radiations originating in our Sun and other heavenly bodies. Cosmic rays comprise the highest energy radiations we know, containing energies larger than any we can generate in our laboratories. (S. F. Singer)

was not the origin of the phenomenon. Strange radiations called *cosmic rays* were designated as the culprits.

Further research showed that these rays can pierce three feet of lead or 3,000 feet of water. The physicists claimed that anything coming in from space with that much energy must certainly originate in the Sun. They added that cosmic rays are radiations similar in nature to light; this theory was quickly disproved when it was shown that cosmic rays, unlike light, are deflected by a magnetic field. Today it is believed that cosmic rays are electrically charged particles bearing extremely high energies. They are said to include protons and atomic nuclei stripped of their electrons. The cosmic nuclei probably exist in the same relative numbers as do the different atoms on Earth, in fact, cosmic-ray particles as heavy as iron and tin have been identified.

Primary cosmic rays enter the atmosphere near the speed of light. They arrive with energies higher than any other known in nature, ranging up to one half a foot-pound per particle. When cosmic rays collide with oxygen or nitrogen atoms in the atmosphere, the energy of the ray is dissipated as the atom is disintegrated, and *mesons* and other types of particles are formed. (Mesons are particles with either a positive or negative charge and with a mass about 200 times that of an electron.) These are the cosmic-ray secondaries whose energy and mass are absorbed by the atmosphere and Earth. Compared with the energy sent to us by the Sun, the total energy of the cosmic rays is equivalent to that of starlight, yet the cosmic-ray mass falling to Earth per minute can easily be contained in a pin point.

It is not known where cosmic rays come from. They could originate in the Sun or in interstellar space or in both places. Neither is it known why mainly high-energy cosmic rays arrive here; the rays seem to be cut off below a certain energy level. Does this mean that they are deflected by the Earth's magnetic field, or that the low-energy rays do not exist? In studying cosmic-ray densities from the equator to 56 degrees latitude, scientists find that the density increases tenfold, yet from 56 degrees to the geomagnetic pole, the density is constant. It is not known why. The answers to these questions could perhaps give us the key that would unlock the structure of the nucleus and lead to an understanding of the true nature of elementary particles.

Daily variations in the ionosphere cause variations in the strength and direction of the Earth's magnetic field. Quite independent of these are variations caused by magnetic storms. The reasons for these storms are being studied, and a connection with sun spots has already been shown.

Looking at the Sun through a telescope, suitably shaded, we often see its surface pockmarked with sun spots. These are dark circular patches sometimes reaching a diameter of 100,000 miles. They are cooler regions than the rest of the Sun, and are sources of great magnetic fields. What is interesting about the sun spots is that sometimes we can see many of them, sometimes none at all. These periods correspond to the *sun-spot maximum* and the *sun-spot minimum*. The entire sun-spot cycle takes 11 years.

The odd characteristic about magnetic storms is that they occur most strongly during a time of sun-spot maximum. Yet they do not appear at the moment a sun spot is seen, and this fact could be said to be an odd coincidence, except that the storms come in a series. They start with a small magnetic disturbance, then 27 days later there is a larger disturbance, and so on, building up to a maximum in 27-day steps, and then back down to a minimum. The rotational period of the Sun is 27 days. Despite our present inability to see them emerge, it is thought that just before magnetic storms take place, vast clouds of ionized particles speed out from the Sun. These storms are world-wide, and could be produced by the electromagnetic effects of these particles streaming past the Earth's magnetic field.

One manifestation of magnetic storms, often of great beauty, is known in the Northern Hemisphere as the *aurora borealis*, in the Southern Hemisphere as the *aurora australis*. We shall speak of the aurora borealis as that one is the more familiar. Although these auroras are usually confined to the upper northern regions, they can sometimes be seen as far south as Washington, D.C., though not in anywhere near their full glory. A typical aurora appears at dusk. It tints the sky with a yellowish- or greenish-white almost eerie glow. Later the glow brightens, gathers itself into a band and arcs east to west across the sky. Soon part of the band may break away into sweeping curves, or may wind around in the sky in serpentine formation; the other part falls into many smaller bands and dancing segments. Sometimes fans of pink, purple and red appear, complete with darkened centers. Around midnight we can see long beams of light falling toward the horizon like folds in a thick drapery. A few hours from dawn the light slowly diffuses and quickly fades away.

A generally accepted theory is that the auroras are located in the ionosphere. Like the magnetic storms, of which the auroras are the visible part, they are caused perhaps by protons speeding from the Sun into the Earth's magnetic field. These particles sweep into the magnetic funnels at the poles. The protons unite with free electrons to form hydrogen, emitting light rays in the process. The later kaleidoscopic patterns are formed by beams of charged particles bombarding the ionized gases in the ionosphere, an action similar to the ionic bombardment of neon in a neon tube.

Closely associated with the auroras is the night air glow. Though usually perceived by instruments, it accounts for 40 per cent of the light in the night sky, apart, of course, from moonlight and starlight. This figure does not take account of the invisible radiations present. It is said that if our eyes were sensitive to the infrared, the air glow would make the night sky as bright as mid-twilight.

As with the aurora, the air glow is caused by ionized particles in the atmosphere, probably in the ionosphere. Some authorities believe that it results from the transfer of some of the energy stored up from sunlight during the day into radiations in the infrared, visible, and ultraviolet during the night. As an example, during the day the sunlight dissociates molecular oxygen. Partial recombination of the resulting atoms during the night involve processes in which light may be emitted. One criticism of this theory is that it is difficult to imagine only such a small part of the Sun's daylight energy being reconverted. If the process is going to take place at all, it has the entire energy in the ionosphere to draw upon.

The Sun holds sway over a number of satellites—planets, asteroids or minor planets, comets, and meteors. Of these, the meteors or "shooting stars" call for our attention for we shall certainly have to contend with them minutes after artificial satellites leave the Earth. The origin of meteors and of their larger brothers, the meteorites, which are different only because they had the good fortune to reach the Earth, is open to speculation. One idea about which many science-fiction writers like to wrap their plots, and that has some scientific backing, says that the asteroids, comets, and meteors were once part of a planet between Mars and Jupiter. Long ago this planet was destroyed either by the tidal forces of Jupiter or by some other catastrophic force. Left in the lost planet's orbit was a ring of asteroids, particles of which sometimes enter our atmosphere as meteors. This story is somewhat plausible, because if we assume a planet in the orbit of the asteroids then, except for Mercury, the distance between each planet is always double the preceding distance. The chemical composition of meteorites also suggests that the material originated in the interior of some large body.

Meteors enter our atmosphere at speeds of about 40 miles per second, a rifle bullet travels less than one mile per second. Turned incandescent by air friction, they streak across the sky with fiery tails up to 30 miles long. They appear much larger than they are because of their envelopes of glowing gases and irradiation effects. Nearly all meteors have diameters far less than one tenth of an inch and weigh less than a few thousandths of an ounce. Of the two types, the stony meteors outnumber the iron meteors ten to one. Although 750 billion particles weighing upwards of one hundred-millionth of an ounce shower the Earth every day, few meteors ever reach the ground. Most of them are so small that despite their great speed, a paper-thin steel body could possibly cruise in space for about a year without ever being pierced. It is doubtful that most meteors could do more harm than dull the surface finish of a tiny orbiting Earth satellite.

The nature of our atmosphere and outer space has been only briefly sketched by science. There are so many questions that man has not answered that those he has seem trivial. It may be better that he not know how much there is still to be known.

Still, to be able to live adequately in our environment and to turn to advantage the energies nature has given us, it is vital that some of the problems be solved. We want to know about the photochemical reactions taking place in the atmosphere. With this information we shall be on our way toward long-range weather forecasting. We want to know the mechanism of the ionosphere and the distribution of ion densities in order to improve radio communications. Cosmic ray, aurora and air-glow studies could give us valuable data about the ultimate nature of particles, and incidentally more information about the generation of nuclear energy. For satellite science and space travel, we need to learn about the winds and turbulences in the upper atmosphere, and about general circulation patterns. It would be a brave crew that would set out on a space journey without also knowing the magnitude and probable frequency of meteor showers.

Upper-atmospheric studies through rocket research have already yielded valuable data. But they are insufficient, and in view of the results, such research has reached the point of diminishing returns.

5.   New Moon

Among the stimulants for raising an Earth satellite are national pride and technical achievement. Those who say that the country that builds the first one will be building military superiority must mean psychological superiority. It is clear that the first satellites will be only probes into the higher altitudes. We cannot use them for guiding missiles. They are too small for tactical mapping, too light for carrying bombs, and too unpredictable for accurate homing. Later, satellites could be part of a weapons system—but now, no.

The United States and the Soviet Union will not have the satellite field to themselves. Other countries will soon begin building their own orbiters. Although the goals will be the same, the means will vary, in fact, the means will vary within a country. For this reason, engineers cannot prescribe a single satellite design and say this is to be.

An artificial Earth satellite is an object that leaves the Earth's surface, ascends to a high altitude where it is held by centrifugal force, and then perhaps descends into the lower atmosphere or to Earth. We say "perhaps" because the satellite may reach an altitude where gravity is not strong enough to bring it back. Then, as with our Moon, the satellite could circle our Earth forever—or at least as long as there is an Earth.

In view of the dimensions of our solar system, the current satellites will not rise very high, only a hop. We know that their return flights to Earth will be disintegrating ones, marked by fiery evaporation as they rush at hypersonic speeds down through the denser atmospheric layers, and a handful of unidentifiable dust will be their remains

When satellites larger than the minimum ones are sent aloft, engineers may try to save them.

The main problem in establishing a satellite is thwarting the pull of gravity. It may be said that our aircraft experience gives us a substantial lead in solving this problem. This statement is not entirely true because the airplane depends for its lift upon the air, which conducts the airplane's weight back to Earth. With it we have no more overcome gravity than has a ship's captain whose vessel is kept afloat by a depth of water. At best, we have constructed a pair of quite high stilts. A satellite, once in its orbit, cannot cry to the atmosphere or to Earth for support; the vehicle must be self-sustaining.

The interplay of gravity and centrifugal force can be pictured if we consider a mass being rotated at the end of a long rubber cord. Given sufficient angular velocity, the centrifugal force keeps the mass in a circular orbit in the plane of the rotating cord. For larger orbits, additional energy must be put into the system to oppose the increased pull of the lengthened cord. A point is finally reached where the amount of energy put into the system is more than the system can contain. The string then tears apart and the freed mass goes speeding off in a way similar to that of a satellite escaping from the Earth's gravitational field.

It must be remembered that the Earth's gravitational field has no sharp boundary; rather its influence is strongest at the Earth's surface; with increasing altitude, the field slowly becomes weaker. This observation is expressed by Newton's inverse-square law, which states that the gravitational force between two bodies varies directly as the product of their masses and inversely as the square of the distance between them. From this law, the acceleration effect of gravity on a 200-mile satellite is 29 ft/sec^2, which is nine tenths of its sea-level value of 32.2 ft/sec^2. For a 4,000-mile satellite, gravity's effect has decreased to 8 ft/sec^2, one quarter of its sea-level value. At the mean altitude of the Moon, which is 238,000 miles from the Earth, the pull of the Earth's gravity on a small mass is practically zero.

We are not seeking to escape the Earth's gravity. That we can is voiced by some of the more optimistic scientists. That we want to, even if we could, is open to serious question. The outer fringes of our atmosphere offer enough data to keep all of today's available scientists busy for all their available time. With our present technology, we could possibly send a small slug of matter bounding into space. Beyond the satisfaction we would get by knowing that we had added a particle to the cosmic dust, there would be little that we could learn from the costly experiment—except lessons in rocket architecture.

The *escape velocity* (speed needed for a body to escape from the Earth's gravity) for a vehicle leaving for outer space is 25,000 miles per hour. This velocity may be produced entirely at the moment of launching or in stages during the vehicle's travel through the atmosphere. We have seen that the stage principle is the preferred one. The escape velocity is calculated through an equation in which the vehicle's initial *kinetic energy,* energy arising from the vehicle's speed, is set equal to the vehicle's final *potential energy,* energy needed to raise the vehicle through the Earth's gravitational field. Since the pull of gravity decreases with increasing heights, the required escape velocities also decrease with height. On this basis, we might ask for a powerful first-stage rocket that would propel its vehicle to perhaps 100 miles' altitude, followed by a second-stage rocket that could then operate on a smaller escape velocity. However, the weight penalty incurred by using such a powerful first stage would more than offset the small decrease in escape velocity; in fact, this velocity is far less than one would intuitively expect, having decreased from its sea-level value only 5 per cent. For a launching site 1,000 miles high, the decrease in gravity still would prescribe a formidable 22,000 miles per hour for escape.

Gravity causes only a part of the resisting force. Another one, almost as great, is air resistance, or drag. This factor depends on the vehicle's shape passing through the atmosphere, the vehicle's velocity and the air density. For a given vehicle and velocity, the drag varies directly with air density, which is small at 100 miles' altitude. Although at this altitude the escape velocity is not significantly changed, the low air drag appreciably lessens the energy needed by a vehicle we want to leave the Earth. These same factors affect the satellite, and its launching at altitude, as in balloon launching, is therefore being studied.

Provided its kinetic energy were high enough to overpower gravity and drag, an object could orbit at any altitude around the Earth. For a sea-level orbit, the gravity requirement calls for an 18,000 mile-per-hour velocity, a speed at which atmospheric drag consumes in just a few seconds all but the most robust meteors. However, air density decreases rapidly for relatively small increases in altitude; at 200 miles the density comes close to zero. Since gravity lessens only slightly at this altitude, we can expect a 200-mile satellite to travel around the Earth at a speed slightly less than 18,000 miles per hour.

It would be strange indeed if the actual orbit of a satellite were a circle. For it to be a circle, we must be assured of two quite difficult happenings: first, when a satellite is launched from its vehicle at orbital altitude, it is launched precisely parallel to the Earth's surface, and second, its launching velocity corresponds exactly with that required to balance the gravitational field. A deviation in either of these factors would result in an elliptic orbit.

If a satellite is not launched parallel to the Earth, then the *perigee*, orbital point nearest Earth, will be closer to the Earth than the launching point, and the *apogee*, orbital point farthest from Earth, will be at a greater altitude than the launching point. If the launching angle is projected up from the horizontal, then the satellite will pass through the apogee before it passes through the perigee. The reverse happens if the launching angle is downward. If the angle is too great, then the orbit will go through the denser atmosphere or into the Earth.

When a satellite is launched parallel to the Earth but slower than is required, its launching point will be its apogee, and its perigee will be halfway around the world—unless the velocity is too slow, in which case the satellite will fall to Earth. When the velocity is more than the altitude requires, then the launching point will be the perigee. Should the velocity exceed the escape velocity, then the satellite will leave the jurisdiction of the Earth never to return.

We are now in a position to appreciate some of the problems that face the creators of an artificial satellite. One of these men, Homer Newell, Jr., director of scientific experiments for *Project Vanguard*, points out that first the satellite must be carried above the appreciable atmosphere, to about 200 miles' altitude. Then the satellite must be projected as close to the horizontal plane as guidance accuracy permits, and with sufficient velocity to assure the satellite's remaining at altitude throughout its orbit. By designing the propulsion system to give with certainty more than enough velocity, engineers can solve the altitude problem. The guidance problem is more difficult. If, for launching altitudes in the range from 200 to 300 miles,

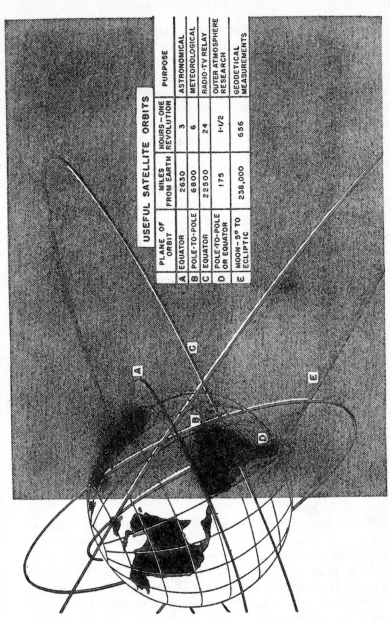

PLANE OF ORBIT	MILES FROM EARTH	HOURS — ONE REVOLUTION	PURPOSE
A EQUATOR	2630	3	ASTRONOMICAL
B POLE-TO-POLE	6800	6	METEOROLOGICAL
C EQUATOR	22500	24	RADIO-TV RELAY
D POLE-TO-POLE OR EQUATOR	175	1-1/2	OUTER ATMOSPHERE RESEARCH
E MOON — 5° TO ECLIPTIC	238,000	656	GEODETICAL MEASUREMENTS

USEFUL SATELLITE ORBITS

Each utility of a satellite prescribes an optimum orbit. The more useful ones that may be within reach of tomorrow's if not today's technology are shown. (Martin, Baltimore) the angle of projection misses the true horizontal plane by as little as 1.5 degrees, the perigee altitude will be roughly half the launching altitude. Such an error occurring with a launching altitude of 200 miles or less would cause the satellite to dip into the denser parts of the atmosphere, and would cut short the satellite's lifetime. For launchings between 200 and 300 miles, which are the likely altitudes for early experiments, engineers will be seeking guidance accuracies well within the 1.5-degree bench mark.

Atmospheric drag, although extremely small in the higher atmosphere, nevertheless collects a toll in energy from every orbiting body. Over a period of time, these payments detract from the speed of the body bringing it closer to Earth. How long a satellite can remain in the sky before spiraling down is an intriguing question. One scientist says that a 200-mile satellite will begin its final descent at the end of 15 days, while another scientist says the interval will range between one and 100 days, depending on the type satellite. Since the characteristics of the atmosphere at extreme altitudes are not accurately known, and since a satellite's orbit will not be learned until it is formed, we can understand the difficulty in making an estimate.

On the basis of upper-atmospheric data gained from rocket research, Dr. Newell believes that a 100-mile altitude satellite would last about an hour. First approximations of the lifetimes of various satellites in near-circular and elliptic orbits have also been calculated by N. V. Petersen of Sperry Gyroscope Company. He estimates that a cylindrical satellite with a cross-sectional area of one square foot and weighing 44 pounds would remain in a 190-mile circular orbit for 47 days. In an elliptic orbit, 62 miles at the perigee and 621 miles at the apogee, the lifetime would be about five hours; for the same apogee but for the perigee increased to 124 miles, the lifetime would jump to about 33 days.

Different orbits are desired for different experiments. These orbits have been roughly classified into three types: equatorial, polar, and intermediate. For the first type, the satellite would orbit in the equatorial plane, and the Earth's rotation would simply cause a change in the satellite's apparent time of revolution. The placement of observing stations on the ground would be particularly easy here because the satellite would always be above the equator. For the polar orbit, the Earth's rotation would cause the satellite's track over the ground to spiral around in a complicated fashion. Only at the poles could we always count on a passage of the satellite overhead once per revolution. It is clear that locating observing stations for a polar orbit would present some difficulties. For the intermediate orbit, the satellite's track over the ground would wind around in a sort of sine wave between a maximum latitude north, and an equal maximum latitude south. The equatorial crossing points, or nodes, would move along the equator in a way depending mainly on the Earth's rotation, but also somewhat on the rotation of the orbital plane caused by the Earth's oblateness. In the intermediate case, also, the setting up of ground stations would be troublesome, the difficulty becoming more pronounced as the inclination of the orbit to the equator was increased.

The early satellites will probably be sent on pole-to-pole or on near-equatorial orbits. In the first-type orbit, a 200-mile satellite would travel once around the world every 90 minutes. In the second-type orbit, if the satellite were launched eastward from the equator, the period would seemingly be greater than 90 minutes owing to the 1,000 mile-per-hour eastward rotation of the Earth, while for a westward equatorial launching, the satellite's period would appear to be less than 90 minutes.

The 200-mile orbit is noteworthy only because it is the easiest to attain. Other orbits of particular value include one at 1,075 miles, which represents the two-hour orbit proposed for the von Braun space station. Petersen considers this altitude the lower limit for a permanent orbit. The 24-hour orbit, which would have the satellite appearing stationary to an observer on Earth, is found at 22,300 miles, and a satellite in this orbit could serve as a radio or TV relay station since three such stations could see more than four fifths of the Earth's surface. Especially valuable for geodetical measurements would be an elliptic orbit stretching 238,000 miles to the Moon. A satellite in this orbit could make one of these round trips every 27⅓ days.

Minimum instrumented satellites have been suggested ever since World War II. On May 4, 1954, the *Mouse* satellite design was revealed at The American Museum-Hayden Planetarium in New York. (*See illustration facing page 144.*) Although Dr. Fred Singer did not know it at the time, his proposal was destined for worldwide attention. In several ways, *Project Vanguard* differs from Dr.

Singer's concept of the satellite—but that the project is worth while and feasible he proved to everyone's satisfaction.

He named the satellite the *Mouse*, which not only gives an indication of its unpretentious size but also, if one wishes to interpret its initials, stands for *Minimum Orbital Unmanned Satellite of the Earth*. He said it would be expendable. It would circle the Earth at a low altitude of about 200 miles, and its life would be short, perhaps only a few days. But above all, the satellite would weigh less than 100 pounds. In brief, the proposal consisted of the concept of an instrument-carrying satellite that would pursue astrophysical and other upper-atmospheric studies.

At the time, the orbit of the *Mouse* was different from the orbits being proposed for other satellites. The *Mouse* would not follow the equator but instead would travel over the poles on a great-circle route and in a plane perpendicular to the Sun-Earth line. It would also cover the whole range of latitudes, as this type of survey is important for determining the energy spectrum of cosmic radiations. In this orbit, too, the satellite would traverse the auroral zones surrounding the poles.

The poles and the regions in the vicinity of the poles would represent the logical places for observing the *Mouse* and for checking its orbit; and most important, for receiving data from the satellite, or for influencing its operation by means of a signal transmitted from the ground.

The orientation stability of the *Mouse* was to be achieved by rotating it about a horizontal axis before take-off. After the third-stage rocket had burned out and the nose tip opened, the spinning cylinder which would be the *Mouse* would be ejected into its orbit around the Earth.

During flight, the spin axis would always be horizontal and at right angles to the direction of motion of the center of gravity. Through the law of conservation of angular momentum, it can be shown that the spin axis will stay horizontal without using any further controlling forces. The instruments would be mounted in two short rods extending through each side of the *Mouse* along the spin axis. The instruments, therefore, would stay fixed in space, which is important from the point of view of interpreting the observations.

The suggested orbit was such that the satellite would always be exposed to the Sun, and a particular half of the satellite would al-

ways see the Sun. This would make the use of a solar power supply
look quite promising.

Since the *Mouse* would pass over the poles every 45 minutes, we
could have patrol planes operating in each polar region. When the
satellite appeared overhead, the nearest plane would send an interrogating radio signal to the vehicle, which would automatically turn
on its radio transmitter. For the next half a minute the satellite would
transmit the information it had recorded during the preceding 45
minutes, which means it would transmit during one per cent of the
time of its travel. Thus, it would collect data for 45 minutes in its
travel from pole to pole, and would transmit for the half minute it
was in the vicinity of each pole. The technical problem could be
solved in a simple way by recording the information on a magnetic
tape moving slowly at 1/30 of an inch per second; 45 minutes could
be recorded on only 7½ feet. Played back at three inches per second,
all the information would be transmitted in 30 seconds.

In a later report, Dr. Singer proposed general principles for designing minimum orbital satellites (MOS). These principles were
based on the need for making best use of the available pay load and
of the orbit type. From these two factors would stem the satellite's
instrumentation and resulting data. MOS was divided into three
groups of increasing propulsion difficulties: I, II, and III. In general,
pay load would be traded for a polar orbit (instead of the easier
equatorial orbit), or for a means of orientating (for example, by
spinning), or for telemetering storage. This is not a rigorous division, but depends to a great extent on changes in the art of instrumentation. Dr. Singer's classification given below is based on the use
of a solar battery.

Difficulty of Propulsion	MOS Pay load (approx.)	Type Orbit	Orien- tation	Telemetering
I	10 lb	equatorial	no	continuous
II	30 lb	equatorial	no	continuous
	25 lb	equatorial	no	triggered or stored
	25 lb	equatorial	yes	continuous
	20 lb	polar	no	triggered or stored
	15 lb	polar	yes	triggered or stored

Difficulty of Propulsion	MOS Pay load (approx.)	Type Orbit	Orien- tation	Telemetering
III	50 lb	equatorial	no	triggered or stored
	50 lb	equatorial	yes	continuous
	40 lb	equatorial	yes	triggered or stored
	40 lb	polar	no	triggered or stored
	30 lb	polar	yes	triggered or stored

One way to keep a satellite's weight low, but still have it instrumented, is to do away with its housing. Dr. I. M. Levitt, director of
The Fels Planetarium, has proposed a satellite weighing about 10
pounds. It would consist of a large deflated rubber balloon or plastic
bag in which a carbon-dioxide cartridge similar to that used to charge
water would be placed. A timing mechanism would be fastened to
the carbon-dioxide cartridge and at a preset instant a triggering
mechanism would release the gas in the cartridge, permitting it to
inflate the balloon. This would take place after the pay load had attained circular velocity. Surrounding the balloon would be a layer
of thin aluminum foil with the shiny surface on the outside. When
the balloon expanded to about 10 feet in diameter, an aluminum
shell of the same diameter would be formed. After the shell had been
inflated, the gas would leak out. However, since there would be no
forces acting on the distended aluminum shell, it would persist as a
sphere.

Built by *Popular Science Monthly* after consulting with scientists
connected with *Project Vanguard,* an 18-inch model of an artificial
Earth satellite was put on display in late 1955 at the Hayden Planetarium and at the Museum of Science and Industry in Chicago's Jack-
son Park. One of the problems being solved by the designers of the
Vanguard satellites is the method of installing much necessary
equipment into such a small sphere. The model made by editors Herbert Johansen and Herbert Pfister showed the equipment
mounted on three mutually perpendicular intersecting disks. Comprising a unit, these disks were placed into a hemisphere and locked
home by a mating hemisphere. The 25-pound models used standard
subminiature electronic parts to denote instrumentation able to make
five upper-atmospheric studies. A simulated mercury battery was

shown as the power source. The model, displayed on a truncated
third-stage rocket, was attached to the top of the rocket by an explosive bolt.

When we come to the *Vanguard* satellites, probably the first practical orbiters to be launched, we enter an area necessarily characterized by compromise. Many conflicting requirements must somehow
be reconciled. Commander Hoover has indicated some of these. The
satellite must be as large as possible, in order that it be easily tracked
by optical means—the larger the object, the greater its visibility. On
the other hand, weight considerations demand that the satellite be
as small as possible. Thus a compromise must be reached in order to
build an object light enough to be successfully placed in an orbit,
large enough to be useful scientifically, and yet small enough to fit
into the nose of the third-stage rocket. Other considerations in designing the satellite develop from the physical stresses it must undergo.
The satellite must be strong enough to withstand the loads imposed
upon it by each of three stages of rocket firing, and this strength must
be gained without excessive weight.

It is known that meteoric dust at the altitudes to be traversed by
the satellite will cause some deterioration to the vehicle's surface.
The rate and extent of the harm are not known, and in fact, one of
the objects of the experiments is to learn the density of meteoric
dust in space. This dust might score the satellite's surface to an extent that would affect its ability to reflect light, thereby affecting the
inside temperature of the satellite and hampering optical tracking.
The engineering assumptions that have been made to arrive at design specifications might be changed when the satellite gets beyond
the atmosphere and is acted upon by meteoric dust. We cannot know
until after the first satellite is fired.

Based on the *Vanguard* satellite's being a thin metallic sphere 20
inches in diameter and weighing only 21.5 pounds, we can appreciate the amount of miniaturizing needed and engineering planning
involved. About half the satellite's weight will be given to structure,
leaving only half for the instrumentation including the telemetering
system. Still, 10 to 11 pounds of small electronic components appropriately devised can yield much vital data. While in its orbit, the
satellite will undergo extreme temperature changes, being alternately in full sunlight and in the Earth's shadow. The temperature is
estimated to swing from 400 degrees Fahrenheit to below zero. Since

transistors and other miniaturized electronic components are designed for a temperature range from 120 degrees to 40 degrees Fahrenheit, either far more rugged instruments will be used or the present ones effectively insulated.

Because the satellite's orbit is expected to be an ellipse with a 200-mile perigee and an 800-mile apogee, the final projectile must be launched in a direction as nearly horizontal as possible. This fact was already emphasized when it was mentioned that a satellite launching error greater than 1.5 degrees would cut the perigee altitude roughly in half, in this case to 100 miles. At this altitude, the satellite would dip into the denser atmosphere, probably never to rise again.

In choosing Patrick Air Force Base at Cocoa, Florida, as the launching site, the Navy and Air Force have the advantage of a near-equatorial orbit and projecting the satellite in an eastward direction adds the speed of the rotating Earth to that of the satellite. The orbit of the satellite will make about a 40-degree angle with the equator. "Both technical and functional considerations were involved in the choice," according to Dr. Kaplan, IGY chairman. "Because optical measurements will play an important role in observations of the satellite, intermediate latitudes appeared desirable, because the opportunities to observe the satellite by many nations over its entire course are thereby enhanced. In terms of observational stations, a true equatorial orbit provides simplicity as against a true polar orbit."

The near-equatorial orbit of a *Vanguard* satellite will send it around Earth in a latitude range about 40 degrees on each side of the equator. While the satellite revolves about the Earth about once every 90 minutes, the Earth rotates beneath. Since the Earth rotates on its axis once every 24 hours, it would have presumably made about one sixteenth of a revolution every time the satellite orbits once. If the orbit of the satellite were circular, then this one-sixteenth-of-a-revolution figure, or 22.5 degrees, would be about right. However, since the orbit is to be elliptical, more than one sixteenth of a revolution will be made by the Earth during one revolution of the satellite. The total displacement of the satellite during succeeding passes across the equator will be about 25 degrees. Thus after one revolution, the satellite will appear about 25 degrees west of its launching point, 50 degrees west on its second passage and so forth. This means that over the course of many revolutions, the orbit of the satellite will shift within a band between 40 degrees north and 40 degrees south of the Earth's equator. The Denver–Philadelphia line lies close to 40 degrees north latitude.

For an orbit angling across the equator, the bulge of the Earth introduces a complication. Because it is not round but oblate, the Earth's diameter is 26 miles longer at the equator than at the poles. This excess mass attends a slightly larger gravity pull, which will distort the orbital plane such that it will gradually rotate in space. This factor and that of having an intermediate orbit compound the tracking problem.

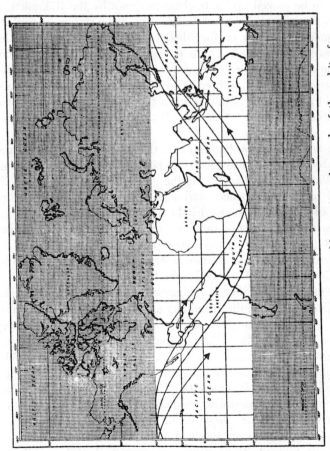

Chiefly because of the Earth's rotation, the track of the orbit of a *Vanguard* satellite will be displaced 25 degrees westward on every succeeding pass across the equator. (IGY–National Academy of Sciences)

Two important advantages stem from the proposed satellite's orbit. First, the satellite's instruments will be able to record observations over a broad expanse of the high atmosphere. Such coverage is important in the IGY program, since the primary objective of this co-operative study is to secure data over the Earth and its atmosphere. Second, the excellent band-width coverage will permit the scientists from a large number of countries to make observations and take measurements.

Radio observations will extend the range for observing the *Vanguard* satellites. The system calls for a satellite transmitter whose signals can be picked up for tracking purposes by the IGY participating nations. The nature and design of the radio system, as well as the frequencies, are to be furnished to all nations. The probable maximum range of these signals is expected to be between 1,000 and 3,000 miles in all directions, depending upon the satellite's altitude. Reasonably good position determinations of a satellite's location could probably be obtained when the transmitter is within 800 miles of the receiver.

In his book *Nineteen Eighty-Four*, the English novelist George Orwell sketched a satirical picture of people living in a totalitarian world. Watching the citizens was the government, which knew all and saw all that happened, and was "affectionately" called *Big Brother*. In the same vein of grisly humor, the engineers working on a proposed reconnaissance satellite have given it the code name *Project Big Brother*. The companies reported to be working on this satellite are the Radio Corporation of America, the Columbia Broadcasting Company, and Lockheed Aircraft Corporation.

According to the syndicated columnists Joseph and Stewart Alsop, this satellite could be of direct military aid. It could fly over Communist bloc countries, take pictures of ground installations, telemeter the facsimiles back to the military in the United States. "The images, it is believed, will be sufficiently clear and detailed to register such major military activity as air base construction or fleet movement. And it will give a sure 'fix' on existing Communist bases, whose location cannot be determined with absolute certainty by present methods." The target date for completion of *Big Brother* is 1961.

The problems that must be solved before this strategic satellite is launched are difficult. They encompass severe technical and diplomatic questions, whose answers must be learned within the next five years. The satellite will be heavy, much heavier than the *Vanguard* satellite. One hundred pounds would be an optimistic guess. In this weight, besides the structure, will be included the weight of the camera and telescope. The camera will be programed to take pictures only when it is over militarily important terrain. There must be a means of storing the pictures until they are ready to be sent to ground observers. Then, the pictures will be telemetered to Earth. Beyond these requirements is the need for a sure source of relatively large power. A solar battery, which derives its energy from the Sun and in turn feeds a storage battery, might suffice. Nuclear energy could be used, but can we quickly build an atomic power plant weighing less than 50 pounds, which is probably the upper limit for this component?

Next we ask about the orbit. If we use a polar orbit, which is the best one since we shall be able to get a complete traverse of the Earth's area, we shall not be able to take advantage of the Earth's rotation as the *Vanguard* satellite will be doing. This factor bears directly on the power of the rockets that must be used—more powerful ones for nonequatorial orbits.

Finally, we ask the diplomats' question. Will the launching of *Big Brother* also launch President Eisenhower's "open sky" policy? Or will it create an international rift?

Of more immediate importance to us are the scientific data that our small basketball satellites will be sending to Earth. These data will be used throughout our technology to ease and add more years to our lives. For these benefits, we must learn much. Before we learn, we must devise the instruments.

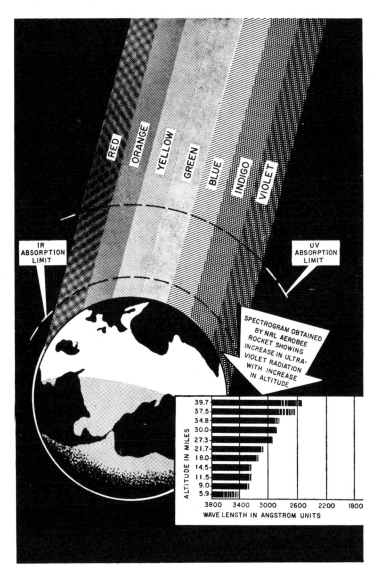

The atmosphere shields us from the Sun's more intense rays. It begins filtering the ultraviolet radiations at about 70 miles' altitude, and the infrared radiations at about 25 miles' altitude. (Martin, Baltimore)

6. Telegram from Outer Space

Hopefully, man shoves his tiny ball of gadgets into space. Crudely it samples the crisscrossing energies, some of which come to it from infinity. The data are sent down to Earth, where scientists begin sorting and interpreting the information. With this beginning, from this microcosm set in the cosmic vastness, a new theory of the universe and of creation may begin to evolve.

Our first venture into space began in June, 1946, when the first V-2 that was instrumented for upper-air research rose 67 miles into the sky. It was launched by the Naval Research Laboratory, which, on the basis of its experience, was chosen for instrumenting the satellite for *Project Vanguard*. The background that NRL had for this responsibility is quite impressive. Starting with the inception of its upper-atmospheric research program in early 1946, the scope and intensity of NRL's work increased to a point where now the laboratory has two branches, Rocket Sonde and Rocket Development, actively engaged in high-altitude projects research. In addition, the Optics Division conducts a full research program of its own on solar radiation and the upper atmosphere. These and other divisions collaborate freely in providing the instrumentation and services required for the continued success of the program. Approximately 60 scientists are involved in different phases of NRL's work—about 40 physicists, and 20 others including electronic scientists, electrical engineers, radio engineers, electronic engineers, and mathematicians.

On January 16, 1947, a meeting of about 50 representatives of more than a dozen interested agencies was convened at NRL to discuss a continuing V-2 program and to devise a means for co-ordinating the work. This group organized itself into the *V–2 Upper Atmosphere Rocket Research Panel*. Membership was restricted to persons actually working on the program. Since the initial formation of the panel, the *Aerobee* and *Viking* rockets have become available, and in March, 1948, the scientific group became known as the *Upper Atmosphere Rocket Research Panel*.

After six years, the V–2 phase of the program ended for a very practical reason. There were no more flyable V–2s left. The V–2 had not been designed to be stored, but to be used as a weapon within a few days after it had been assembled. That it could be stored for years and still be usable is a tribute to the Germans' technical abilities. It has been estimated that during their research activities, the V–2s carried more than 20 tons of instruments to altitudes ranging from 50 to 100 miles. Because of the original design concept, the V–2 was far from an ideal upper-air research vehicle. When instruments replaced the V–2's warhead, the center of gravity of the missile moved aft and its stability was destroyed. To bring the center of gravity forward, lead ballast had to be put into the nose, thereby taking up valuable instrument volume.

When the Navy saw that the V–2 stockpile was almost exhausted, they initiated the design of a new rocket—the *Viking*. The Martin Company of Baltimore was called in to help develop the vehicle. This was to be the first practical rocket specifically designed to probe the upper atmosphere. Much valuable data were taken during the *Viking* tests. Knowledge was gained about the electron density in the ionosphere. Solar radiations were investigated away from the blinds of the lower atmosphere. Cosmic rays left their traces on specially treated film. Pressures and densities were measured up to 80 miles' altitude.

Despite the success of the *Viking* project, a twig had been fashioned to do the work of a crowbar. Since at the higher altitudes the obstacle-free molecular path is of the order of magnitude of the *Viking's* length, the rocket was enshrouded in its own exhaust. The instruments were constantly being asphyxiated by the vehicle's gases, which escaped from the thrust chamber and from other unpressurized chambers into the rarefied atmosphere, and they came from seething battery fluids and from unconsumed propellants. Above 90 miles, the temperature, pressure, and density data taken by the *Viking* are meaningless.

The *Aerobee* project, sponsored by the Navy Bureau of Ordnance and the Office of Naval Research, and directed by the Applied Physics Laboratory of The Johns Hopkins University, called for an inexpensive rocket, ten of which would equal the cost of one *Viking*. The *Aerobee* was devised to carry 150 pounds to about 70 miles. The design philosophy stated that if only one investigation were carried out on each flight, then ten investigations could be run for the cost of one *Viking* launching. All efforts could be concentrated on the study at hand. With different instruments being installed to measure and check the same physical phenomenon, no conflicting interests would jam the data-taking. Propulsion is carried out in two stages, first by a solid-propellant booster rocket that falls away when spent, and then by a liquid-propellant sustaining rocket motor that is spent at about 18 miles' altitude. The rocket motor burns a mixture of red-fuming nitric acid and an alcohol solution. Since 1948, NRL has directed 20 firings, and conducted 31 upper-air experiments, which include five cosmic-radiation, 14 solar radiation, three pressure, three temperature, four composition, one ionosphere, and one photographic.

There are drawbacks to the *Aerobee*. It is a low-altitude probe. It is fin-stabilized, which means that wind and ballistic calculations must be made and must be optimum to assure successful launching. In addition, the required minimum pay load of 120 pounds prevents a weight-for-altitude trade.

During 1953 and 1954 the small *Deacon* rocket was joined with the giant *Skyhook* plastic balloon to produce the *Rockoon*. The *Deacon* rocket has a severely limited pay load of 50 pounds. Yet with fair accuracy, physicists have been able to devise experiments giving data on upper-atmospheric pressure, temperature, density, and solar radiations. Since *Rockoons* are cheap—only $2,000 each—and can be launched from nearly any accessible location, 120 of them are scheduled for use during the IGY.

The drawbacks of the *Aerobee* led to the development of the *Aerobee-Hi*. Sponsored by the Air Force and the Navy, and designed by Aerojet-General Corporation, this vehicle could be the last rocket sounding device before a satellite is launched. The *Aerobee-Hi* has ascended to 180 miles with a pay load of 150 pounds. To lessen the amount of gas escaping from its interior, the vehicle is completely pressure-sealed. Since the *Aerobee-Hi* is equipped with

nose and body parachutes, there is the possibility that the same vehicle can be used for several flights. This arrangement means that
compact recording equipment is able to replace the more bulky
and weight-consuming telemetering equipment. The handling and
launching of the *Aerobee-Hi* is much simpler than that of the original
Aerobee, which in turn is vastly simpler than the techniques needed
for the *Viking.* Forty-five *Aerobee-Hi's* are scheduled to be used for
the Upper Atmospheric Research Program of the IGY.

Despite the success of our upper-atmospheric research programs,
as long as we have to depend solely on rocket vehicles for our data
we shall have to be satisfied with astigmatic glimpses of the higher
altitudes. For mere minutes of data-taking if we are successful, technicians must put in months and years of work. The information we
get from the experiments is to a large extent haphazard, depending
as it does on good weather for launching, and is often gravely ham-
pered by the mechanics of flight. To move our present concept of the
upper atmosphere toward reality, our Pogo-stick research is being
replaced by a semipermanent laboratory in the sky.

Any artificial satellite circumnavigating the Earth can give us vital
physical data. However, even with a thousand satellites flying, there
still would not be enough for their students. Nearly every scientist
has a proposed study for a satellite, which investigation is held to be
the most important. Perhaps the most difficult problems to solve will
be diplomatic ones working out which studies are to be made first.

If a country which is unwilling to share its satellite data is able to
install an orbiting vehicle, then, before we establish our own vehicles,
we shall have to accept *passive* data—data derived purely by observing the satellite. Information gained this way would be by no means
trivial. The satellite loses speed and altitude when it enters the
Earth's atmosphere, and knowing just how much would help us fill
the gaps in our table of upper-atmospheric densities. Perhaps the
upper atmosphere is not a region of steadily decreasing densities but
rather is one composed of peaks and valleys. If the satellite should
behave erratically then this "peak-valley" theory would have backing. Dr. Newell writes that if the satellite's orbit can be accurately
determined, then the satellite can be used as the Moon is used for
geodetic measurements. Observations made of the artificial moon at
different spots on the Earth, either simultaneously or at precisely re-

lated times, can be used to determine the distance on the ground between the observing sites. Also, by measuring the effect of the Earth's oblateness on a satellite moving in an orbit inclined to the equator, it should be possible to determine the actual amount of bulging at the equator. It may be that the nonuniformity in the distribution of mass in the Earth's crust will also cause an observable perturbation in the satellite's orbit; in this event, the effect, which will be much smaller than that caused by the Earth's oblateness, will be analyzed.

When we launch our own satellites, we can count on their active participation in a program contributing essential data to every field of science. We would get the data through the telemetering equipment on board, which would read the instruments for us and relay the information by radio to receivers on Earth. When larger satellites are built, we shall load some of them with cameras and film packets to obtain data difficult or impossible to telemeter. Before it became interred during the last minutes of the satellite, the exposed film would have to be rescued. One method would be that used in the V-2 and *Aerobee* rocket tests. The exposed film was spooled into a hardened steel container. Although the rocket upon impact with Earth would be found crushed and twisted, the film container would be safely guarding its contents. It has been proposed that just before a satellite enters the Earth's atmosphere, an explosive charge be triggered and released inside the satellite. The film package would then be shot free and parachute slowly to Earth. Appropriate for this procedure is the jingle: "I shot an arrow into the air. It fell to Earth, I know not where." It may be that radar tracking would help keep sight of the container, but with the chances of accurate tracking of so small an object being so slim, it is doubtful that the effort is worth the reward.

The more prudent procedure would be to miniaturize further the telemetering equipment in order to send more data per satellite. If photographs taken from the satellite are needed, and it is still not possible to guide the satellite back to Earth, then what may be used is televised transmission of the pictorial data, or facsimile transmission similar to that used for sending news photographs across country. In view of today's technology, facsimile reproduction would probably be used because television transmission demands a satellite power source far greater than we have available.

Before we can derive any data from a satellite, we must know where it is, and we must be able to keep constant track of it. Radar and optical trackers appropriately placed beneath the orbit can do this. When the satellite passes out of the line of sight of one tracking system, the next one takes over. This procedure requires close international co-operation, much closer and more rigorously adhered to than most diplomatic alliances.

Conventional radar tracking stations can tell us the location of the satellite. These stations will not give us the aspect of the satellite, which knowledge could be quite important if some of the instruments had been designed to face the Sun during predetermined intervals. Neither will these stations be able to determine the satellite's velocity or acceleration. For these data, investigators will use a *doppler-radar system*.

The doppler principle can be described by reference to our perception of sound waves. When a sound source approaches a listener, the wave frequency or pitch appears to increase because the number of waves per second encountered increases. Similarly, as a sound source leaves the listener, its pitch appears to decrease. By measuring the apparent change in the waves' frequency, which is equivalent to measuring the change in pitch, the listener has a measure of how fast the sound source is traveling. In an analogous manner, a doppler-radar transmitter sends a high-frequency wave to the satellite and to a ground-based receiver. The satellite retransmits the wave to the same receiver. By comparing the frequencies of the two waves, engineers at the ground-based receiver can learn the satellite's velocity. From the changes in velocity, the engineers can also derive the satellite's acceleration.

Optical tracking is often the most satisfying. By this means, operators can see the satellite, know its aspect, and be assured they are not watching ghosts on a radar screen. An optical instrument that has been used quite frequently for this purpose is the *theodolite*. One version consists of a 25-power telescope that conveys its horizontal and vertical deflections to a magnetic recorder. A more advanced version of the same instrument, the *ciné theodolite*, photographs the flight of the vehicle. A combination of research stations and of conventional radar, doppler radar, optical and special tracking facilities will be used to establish the orbits of satellites. One combined system proposed to the Air Force is called the "Automatic Tracking

Theodolite and Data Analyzing System." First, a radar beam locates and locks itself on a satellite. The theodolite, now knowing where to look so to speak, tracks the satellite. The tracking data are sent from the radar and the theodolite to a magnetic recorder for a permanent record. The recorder then passes the data on to a computer which turns the raw data into information amenable to analysis.

Along with the instruments needed to measure the phenomena being studied, and the tracking and power equipment, a satellite must carry a highly compact telemetering unit. Telemetering is the process of transmitting data from a remote source, usually from an inconvenient or highly inaccessible one. Any gauge on an automobile dashboard displays telemetered data—fuel level, for example, can be seen without the driver's ever having to look into the fuel tank. Telemetered information must be accurately transmitted, received and displayed. Any convenient transmission line can be used, and depending on the circumstances, the line may be hydraulic, pneumatic, electrical or electronic.

The transmission line for the satellite is electronic (radio). The part it plays in a telemetering system can be illustrated by one method of sending temperature data from a satellite to Earth. It is known that the electrical resistance of a wire varies with the temperature of the wire. Through suitable circuitry, the change in electrical resistance of the wire is related to a change in electrical current. This changing current produces corresponding changes in a radio wave which is sent from the satellite to a receiving station on Earth. Here the signal is recorded, and analyzed, and the temperature in the satellite is learned. This process is the same as that of ordinary radio broadcasting. The microphone changes sound energy into electrical energy. The electrical energy modulates a radio frequency wave which is picked up by home receivers, and is heard as program material.

Telemetering systems can be divided into two major types: the *time-division system,* and the *frequency-division system.* In the first system, the physical quantities to be measured are done so on a time-sharing basis. In sequence, each quantity is looked at for a short period of time. When all have been seen, the process is repeated.

In the frequency-division system of telemetering, a continuing transmission of each physical quantity being measured is made. This method is similar to that of radio broadcasting where each station transmits its individual program on its assigned frequency; the link is radio, and the receiver is the radio set tuned to the station of choice.

A source of electrical power is needed for the instrument and telemetering activities on the satellite. To ask today for enough power to operate continuously all the equipment on board would be to ask for a satellite too heavy to launch. Therefore, it has been agreed that only for short intervals during satellites' travels will full power be demanded. In the intervening time, stand-by power will be used. A pretiming device in the satellite could be designed to turn the power on and off at stated intervals. This is a ticklish method; for its correct functioning it requires that we know precisely when a satellite will be in the range of a receiving station. The difficulty is clearer when we realize the problem of even knowing how long the satellite will remain aloft. A second method, and the one which probably will be adopted, involves the satellite's using its stand-by power to store data; then when a receiving station sends an interrogating signal to a satellite, it uses its full power to send these data to Earth.

It has been estimated that a maximum power requirement of 50 watts for three minutes, and a stand-by power of one watt per revolution would be sufficient for most satellite experiments. On the basis of present power equipment, engineers are able to incorporate more than 500 watt-hours of energy into a satellite, which would keep its equipment functioning for about eight days.

If no satellite were expected to live more than a few days, then the power package could be easily furnished by a bank of lightweight batteries already on the market. When a hoped-for life of later satellites is months or even years, then other sources of electrical power must be considered. The nuclear reactor has been proposed as a power source, but even though its shielding could possibly be eliminated for an unmanned satellite, such a reactor with its associated equipment would be far too heavy. From the physicists's point of view, another disadvantage would be the reactor's emission of radiations which would obscure the data being picked up by the instruments.

A second scheme proposes taking advantage of the temperature difference between the shaded and unshaded surfaces of a satellite.

Then by appropriate electrical circuits the difference could be converted into electrical energy. Because of its inefficiency, this system has not received much backing, though a related idea has—and this hinges on the *solar battery*. As implied by its name, the battery derives its energy from sunlight, which every 48 hours pours more energy onto the Earth than is contained in all the known supply of the Earth's fossil fuels. The newest solar batteries can develop a potential of one-half volt, and can deliver about 90 watts for every square yard of exposed surface. It is estimated that this is only half the power that an optimum design could deliver.

Made of a layer of individual silicon wafers, the solar battery has no moving parts or corrosive chemicals. Even in poor light, it can generate energy but at a lower power. Those that are in use now are at least 15 times more efficient than the best solar energy converters. In Americus, Georgia, a solar-battery installation is powering a rural telephone service. Excess current, not needed for immediate telephone use, is fed into a storage battery, which provides power at night and over periods of bad weather.

In contrast to the storage battery, the solar battery has only low power, but it can deliver power for an indefinite length of time. Because a large source of sure power for the lifetime of a satellite is essential, early satellites will be using storage batteries instead of solar batteries. When larger satellites are launched with expected lifetimes measured in months, then a chemical storage battery fed by a solar battery will probably be specified.

Techniques for observing cosmic rays have been well developed in our upper-atmospheric studies with balloons and rockets. One of the research instruments, the Geiger counter, will be installed in a satellite to measure the strength and direction of cosmic primary radiations. The instrument is composed of a long metal tube containing a fine wire running the length of the center line and insulated from the tube. A suitable gas under low pressure fills the tube. The electrical potential between the wire and the tube is set at a value slightly lower than what would allow a current to flow between the metal tube (negative) and the wire (positive). If a single charged particle, such as a cosmic ray, enters the tube, the resistance to current flow is broken down for an instant and there is a current pulse. The Geiger counter can keep track of current pulses up to a maximum of 5,000 pulses per second. Since at satellite altitude the cosmic-ray count is quite large, thereby causing telemetering and power problems, it is probable that a counter will be used that will transmit only every eighth or tenth pulse.

The *Geiger telescope*, which was used in the instrument head of an early V–2, is a more elaborate version of the counter. The telescope not only tells the intensity but also the path of cosmic radiations. Here the counters are arranged in a geometric pattern. If a charged particle goes through all of them "simultaneously," then its direction is known. Its energy can be learned by measuring the particle's penetration of lead plates mounted beneath the counters.

There are even more elaborate cosmic-ray instruments, but because they require cameras or other components that are awkward from the viewpoint of unrecoverable satellites, these instruments will have to await recoverable vehicles. When they are flying, we shall also send up cloud chambers and photographic emulsion plates. It was through the cloud chamber that the positive electron, the *positron*, was discovered. The instrument works on the principle that a charged particle passing through an atmosphere saturated with water vapor leaves behind it a trail of fine droplets of water. By correct lighting and camera orientation, the trail shows up as a white streak on a black background. If two cameras set at right angles to each other are used, a three-dimensional view of the track is seen. In practice, the cloud chamber is flanked on each side by a Geiger counter. When a charged particle has passed through the counters, the vapor-laden atmosphere in the chamber is suddenly supersaturated by the sudden withdrawal of a piston. The ions left by the charged particle act as condensation nuclei and the particle's path is perceived as a streak of water vapor. NRL used this idea to design and construct a cloud chamber specifically tailored for upper-air research with rockets. The chamber was six inches in diameter and contained argon and alcohol-water vapor at about two atmospheres' pressure.

Another chamber, operating with 300 atmospheres' pressure, has been designed by the Brookhaven National Laboratory on Long Island, for cosmic-ray study. It is hoped that this high pressure will stop cosmic rays before they leave the chamber, thereby delineating their fates.

A photographic emulsion plate acts somewhat like a cloud chamber. Having about 2,000 times the stopping power of normal air, it records the full track of all but the most energetic cosmic rays. The tracks are so fine that a microscope must be used to examine them. From their length, the energy content of the rays can be determined. The advantage of using emulsion plates lies in their readiness without triggering to record the passage of charged particles, in their great simplicity, and in their relative lightness. In any form, cosmic-ray research by a satellite will give the atomic physicist invaluable data for his work. It will also tell us whether these rays constitute a potential health hazard to the space traveler or whether, like the fear of so many unknowns, the danger is not so great as we have conceived it.

From a practical point of view, we wish to know the effects of solar radiations on our weather, climate and radio communications. It is believed that these radiations trigger weather processes in the troposphere and cause ionic upheavals in the ionosphere. In order to relate these disturbances to our weather and to our communication networks, we have to have full monitoring of solar activity. From data derived from these studies, we should be able to predict weather more accurately and communicate more efficiently with one another. The economic worth of these investigations cannot be overemphasized.

For his *Mouse* satellite design which in many ways was a forerunner of the *Vanguard* satellite, Dr. Singer proposed carrying out observations and measurements of the changing solar conditions on a continuing basis. He said that a few pounds of instrumentation could show us a detailed picture of the conditions existing during solar disturbances, especially of the Sun's ultraviolet emissions and corpuscular streams, the fast-moving atomic particles. For measuring the solar ultraviolet and X rays, the task would be one of finding how radiation intensities in different wave lengths vary with time. In this way, correlations could be made with sea-level observations of the visible Sun, and with effects produced by the solar ultraviolet and X rays in the Earth's atmosphere. The most fruitful instrument for observing these radiations is the ultraviolet and X-ray photon-Geiger counters that have been used by the NRL in various rocket experiments. These counters are designed to be sensitive only to *photons* (particles of energy) within certain wave-length intervals; for example, some counters can be made sensitive to X rays only. Thus it is possible to find the radiation intensity in the particular region of the solar spectrum being studied.

Nature is so easily influenced that it is not unexpected to find upper-altitude irregularities in the magnetic field. Together with these irregularities is the expected over-all decrease in magnetic-field intensity with altitude. To get these data, Dr. J. P. Heppner of NRL's Rocket Sonde Branch, has proposed measuring the Earth's magnetic field above the E-region of the ionosphere as a possible satellite experiment.

An impetus for his experiment is given by the knowledge that a small but most interesting part of the Earth's magnetic field is caused by current systems flowing in the ionosphere and in outer space. Their fluctuations are believed to cause corresponding fluctuations observed in the Earth's magnetic field at the ground. A current sheet flowing in the neighborhood of 60 miles' altitude, in the E-region, has already been detected. An *Aerobee* rocket launched from a point on the geomagnetic equator March, 1949, recorded a sharp decrease in the magnetic field at that altitude. By satellite measurements, it is proposed to detect the presence of additional current flows in what is called the *Chapman-Störmer current ring*.

This ring encircles our globe in an equatorial belt at several Earth radii from the Earth's surface. Having its genesis in the Sun, the ring is composed of charged particles that the Earth's permanent magnetism has deflected into a ring. As the supply of particles from the Sun varies, so does the effect of the ring upon the surface magnetic field, and the sudden appearance of an intense stream of solar particles produces a pronounced variation in the Earth's magnetic field. One theory holds that particles spraying off from the Chapman-Störmer ring reach the Earth's atmosphere in the auroral zones and cause the aurora.

Heppner's experiment consists in making continuous satellite measurements of the Earth's magnetic field at 200 to 300 miles' altitude, while simultaneous measurements of the magnetic field are made on the ground. With the high-altitude and ground curves available, it should then be possible to estimate the magnitude of current flow in the Chapman-Störmer ring.

Already designed for small-rocket experiments, there exists a lightweight version of a *proton-precession magnetometer,* which will give investigators data on the total magnetic field. This device comprises a plastic tank containing a copper coil immersed in water. When the instrument is operating, a ground signal sent to the appropriate satellite triggers a programmer, which energizes and de-energizes the coil every second. When the coil is energized, the hydrogen nuclei in the water line themselves up like miniature magnets. When the coil is de-energized, the nuclei change their positions, vibrating and precessing into the Earth's magnetic lines of force. The movements of the nuclei are picked up by the copper coil as tiny currents, which are then amplified, coded for transmission, and relayed to ground stations on Earth. By knowing the magnetic field at precise positions in the upper atmosphere, scientists can relate these data to the ground-based data, and determine the characteristics of current flows in the ionosphere.

The number of experiments that can be carried out by satellites are limited most importantly by man's ingenuity, and only secondarily by today's instrumentation. There will certainly be studies of the air-density gradients, the data for these coming from passive observations of the satellite. One thousand tons of micrometeorites a day shower down through the atmosphere onto the Earth, on their way causing minor whirlpools in the ionosphere. These interplanetary dust particles will be sensed by some satellite instrument, probably a simple impact detector or electrostatic analyzer. When satellites become larger or spectrometer apparatus smaller and lighter, then more inclusive experiments will be devised to obtain data about the composition of the upper atmosphere.

Overriding the immediate needs for launching power and instrumentation are those needs connected with society. Every radical invention affects and is affected by the people it serves. It is here that lies the impetus to discovery. What the early and later satellites and space platforms will do to society is by far the most important question that *Project Vanguard* will begin answering.

7.   Observatories in the Sky

The task of planning for the observation of the IGY satellites has been assigned by the National Academy of Sciences to the Smithsonian Astrophysical Observatory. This work involves the precise tracking and timing of the satellites through specially designed telescopes located at 12 or more strategically selected places around the world. These stations cannot begin their highly accurate orbit-determining and data-gathering until after the initial path of the satellite has been plotted, nor can they follow the extremely rapid orbital changes which will occur during the last hours of the satellite.

"The first observations of the satellite after launching, and the last before the satellite spirals to the Earth, will be the most important," says Harvard Professor Fred Whipple, director of the Smithsonian Astrophysical Observatory. "A world-wide corps of sky watchers will be needed." He adds that satellite projects offer amateur astronomers throughout the world an unparalleled chance to be of significant service to science. For this purpose, the nonprofessional groups have been alerted and briefed both about the techniques for observing satellites and about the procedures to be used for reporting their observations. Other professional astronomers also emphasize the need for the amateurs' help, without which much vital data would undoubtedly be lost.

Seeing a satellite in flight will not be an experience restricted to trained observers. Anyone with patience and sharp vision or optical aids will be able to glimpse the orbiting vehicle. We can expect that when it is announced that the first satellite is flying, children's telescopes will be hastily dusted off for use, and opera glasses that have never seen an opera will be quickly rescued from attics all over the world. Charts and graphs describing the probable orbit of the satellite will be studied avidly, and the world will have a corps of ground observers operating that will be the envy of even the most conscientious civil defense organization.

What most of us want to know is the best time for viewing a satellite, and what type of optical aid would give us the best results for the least money. When President Eisenhower first told the world that the United States was planning to build a satellite for the IGY, NRL engineer Dr. Richard Tousey was discussing at a formal conference in Copenhagen, Denmark, the question of the visibility of a hypothetical 21-inch-diameter Earth satellite. He showed that for a 200-mile satellite, a low-powered telescope or almost any binocular would be adequate for viewing. Probably the best compromise, if a single stock instrument is to be used, is the Navy shipboard binocular, which is a standard 7 x 50 binocular with a field of view of seven degrees.

Viewing conditions are best when the satellite, while reflecting the Sun's light, is passing directly overhead in a darkened sky. This is the time just before sunrise or just after sunset. A team of observers would be needed to cover the region of the sky through which the satellite is to pass.

Each observer should monitor a binocular fixed in position and carefully oriented with respect to the approximate orbit of the satellite; the fields covered by adjacent binoculars should not overlap more than is necessary to ensure complete coverage of the sky. Each binocular should be equipped with a right-angle prism over the objective lens to permit the viewer to use his binocular in a normal horizontal position.

Because a satellite can be seen best while the Sun is rising or setting, the optimum viewing time is limited to about 45 minutes for a 200-mile satellite. Under these viewing conditions, the satellite has the brightness of about a *fifth-magnitude star*. Stars are classified according to the relative magnitude of their brightness, with first-magnitude stars being the most brilliant and sixth-magnitude the least brilliant perceived by the naked eye.

There probably will be several stars in the field of view of about the same brightness, and possibly some that are brighter. The presence of these stars will provide helpful reference points that are practically stationary, and that will aid in keeping the observer's eyes

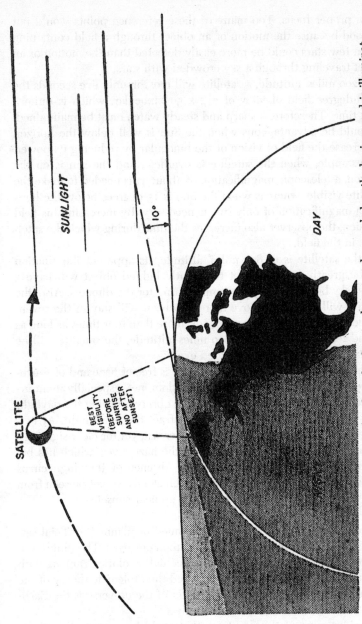

A satellite is seen best at dusk, when the Sun is about ten degrees below the horizon and is illuminating the satellite as it passes overhead.

set in proper focus. Too many of these reference points would not be good because the motion of an object through a field containing only a few stars could be more easily detected than the motion of an object traveling through a sky crowded with stars.

At 200 miles' altitude, a satellite will cross in only five seconds the seven-degree field of view of a 7 x 50 binocular, which is quite a short time. Therefore, a sharp and steady watch must be maintained. It would be advantageous when the Sun is well below the horizon to increase the field of vision of the binocular by reducing its power. For example, when the satellite is overhead and the sun is on the horizon, a telescopic magnification of about 41 is needed to make the satellite visible, whereas when the Sun is 15 degrees below the horizon, a magnification of only two is necessary. By increasing his field of vision, the observer also increases the time during which the satellite is in the field.

If the satellite is at 800 miles' altitude, its apparent illumination will be greatly lessened. Yet the faintly lighted object will have a darker sky behind it, in part compensating for the dimness. Also, the satellite will appear to move more slowly. It will stay in the seven-degree binocular field for 21 seconds, more than four times as long as for the 200-mile satellite. At 800 miles' altitude, the satellite will be impossible to see with the unaided eye.

It has been assumed here that the sky is free of haze and of Earth-sourced lights. These conditions are seldom met, especially in an urban community. It is most serious to the observer during the daylight hours when dust particles in the air refract the Sun's light. At twilight, the Sun's rays miss most of the overcast, yet for clear sightings, the observer should be located above the haze layer, which lies between 5,000 and 10,000 feet altitude. Absence of thin high cirrus clouds is also important. Frequently, such clouds cannot be seen from sea level during the daytime, but show up near sunset.

Astronomy practiced from an unmanned or manned artificial satellite would have profound influences upon our lives. The philosophical aspects alone could cause an intellectual revolution ranking with that caused by Galileo when he disputed the Ptolemaic theory of the universe—the proposition that the center of the universe is the Earth about which the Sun and planets revolve.

Consider some of the questions that could be answered! Is there life on Mars? Telescopic views have shown indications of canal systems on the planet's surface. Depending on which side of the astronomical fence one is on, these may truly be canal systems built by intelligent beings, or else they are natural formations that merely look like such systems.

How are stars born? Are they concentrated accumulates of the dust in the universe, or of the gases? Are they offsprings conceived during nuclear explosions of the mature stars? Perhaps they are the results of a continuing creation. The answer, if obtained, could reinforce or challenge many present-day concepts.

Is the speed of light constant, as most scientists believe? If it is then it is the only constant in our cosmology. Some investigators suggest that light is not as faithful as their colleagues would like to believe. These iconoclasts suggest that light rays after traveling for millions of years might age and experience deterioration.

Astrophysicist Fritz Zwicky, peppery Swiss professor now at the California Institute of Technology, proposes an astronomical study that ranks in scope with determining the speed of light. He suggests using artificial satellites to help us learn how fast gravity acts, which he terms the *speed of gravitational interaction*. He says that after having gone through a highly complicated mathematical study, he believes that gravity acts either at half the speed of light or twice the speed of light, although he does not know which. His conclusion is based on studies of the larger constellations in the universe. If the speed of gravitational interaction were infinite, Professor Zwicky says we should observe clusters of galaxies ever on the increase in size, but we know that there is a limiting size, and therefore there must be a finite speed of interaction. If the speed were equal to the speed of light, then the biggest clusters of galaxies should be 20 million light years in diameter. Yet clusters 50 to 60 million light years in diameter have been seen. If Professor Zwicky's twice-the-speed-of-light figure is proved, physicists will have to do some fast backtracking because one of the truly basic concepts of all of modern physics is that light is absolutely the fastest phenomenon.

In the Mount Palomar Observatory, astronomers are using the much-publicized 200-inch telescope mirror. Probably the largest piece of glass ever made for any reason, the 20-ton mirror's undersurface looks like a huge waffle iron. This design eliminates much weight and allows for placement of supporting structure. The mirrored surface is accurate to within one twentieth of a wave length of light, a specification so rigorous that some experts observed at the time it was built that we have already passed the point of diminishing returns. It took years of planning and building, and weeks of labor to carry the mirror undistorted from the East Coast where it was poured, to the West Coast, and from here to the top of Mount Palomar. That a larger telescope will ever be constructed for use on Earth is extremely doubtful because the internal weight strains alone would be impossible to eliminate to any tolerable degree. Out in space though, with no weight to distort the mirror, the size of a telescope is limited only by our technology. Using a thermoplastic material, a 1,000-inch mirror which would weigh only 150 pounds has been proposed. A more realistic proposal calls for a 40-inch telescope. It is estimated that this instrument suitably placed could see objects one tenth the size of the smallest object seen by the Mount Palomar mirror, and could pick up galaxies five times farther away. If a 100-inch telescope were used, then ten-mile distances on the planet Mars could be distinguished.

The advantage of a space observatory over an earth-bound one is that of looking through clear glasses rather than through fogged ones. Before a planet or star can be seen, its light must first travel through the body's own atmosphere, through space, and then through the Earth's turbulent and sometimes misty atmosphere. Near the Earth's surface, the light rays are often distorted by overcast skies and smog. In fact, the best images we have of Mars, our second closest planet, are badly blurred, and even its major geographic formations are open to controversy. Above the Earth's atmosphere, nearly 99 per cent of the visual problems are solved.

It has been suggested that the space observatory be located in a 1,100-mile altitude orbit. At this height, not only would observations be free from atmospheric interference but also the telescope could be turned toward the Earth to see about one third of its surface. These sightings would be extremely valuable because they would shed light on our observations of other planets. Although it has been stated that installing such a satellite must await a servicing crew in a manned satellite, we doubt that astronomers will restrain themselves that long. Proponents of the unmanned observatory orbiting at perhaps less than desired altitude would argue that even comparatively crude observations are better than none.

All will not be a primrose path for these observatory builders. The telescope will have to be regulated and controlled remotely. It will have to track accurately. These operations require a satellite much heavier than the minimum one, although that is being hailed as the supreme achievement of today's engineers. The instrumentation needed to transfer the telescopic images to a ground station will be a major problem. To these, we can add others. The engineers must design their apparatus against the effects of wide temperature variations. The mirrored surface will have to be protected against meteoric impacts, either by a meteor bumper or by a material impervious to most high-speed meteors, or the station will have to be considered a short-lived probe. Whatever design criteria are used and whatever we calculate the length of the observatory's first life will be, there is no doubt that the observatory will be built and that its future will be unending.

We often find we have not answered even the simplest questions. Here are some sample ones: What is the distance between New York City and Southampton, England? What is the Earth's diameter at the equator and at the poles? What is the value of the Earth's gravitational constant g?

It took until 1954 to learn the distance across the Atlantic Ocean within an accuracy of 1,000 feet. Had there not been a solar eclipse during that year to aid us, we would not have been that close. This inaccuracy is indicative of world-wide inaccuracies in geography. Only recently have we been able to close the thirtieth meridian, and then only after the fullest international co-operation and enormous expense. Europeans handled the survey on the Continent and carried the line through Turkey to connect with the African link. Many times the arc had to be run through flat featureless areas that required either closely spaced sightings, such as those taken during ordinary surveying, or the construction of expensive towers to act as targets. And other times the arc traversed rugged mountains and large expanses of water. How much easier it would have been had the surveyors been able to sight on a close reference point in the sky! They would have needed better accuracy than the Moon as a target could have given them, but an artificial satellite stabilized in its orbit could have increased the Moon-target accuracy by a factor of ten.

Through the satellite, map makers could have learned the distance across the Atlantic within 100 feet instead of 1,000. The technique would have involved taking simultaneous sightings on the satellite from the two points being traversed, then through elementary triangulation methods, the distance between the points could have been easily and economically found.

Life would be much easier for geographers, navigators, prospectors, and a host of other people if our Earth were a sphere. One instance is that of searching for oil fields. It has been estimated that in the United States more than $2.5 billion are spent every year for exploratory diggings. The locations suspected of having oil are chosen on the basis of geological surveys in which gravity plays quite an important role. A variation in gravity from its average g value indicates a variation in the Earth's crustal condition, which may mean the presence of oil or other minerals. But what is the average value of gravity on Earth? As an approximation we use $g = 32.2$ ft/sec^2, but we are sure only that we are not sure.

For a first model we assume that the Earth is a sphere. This is a crude hypothesis because centrifugal force has given a bulge to the equator and has flattened the poles. We are told that the difference in radii from the Earth's center is only 13 miles, but this figure is large enough to cause problems. One problem is whether this 13-mile figure is right. Although we know with sufficient accuracy how fast the Earth rotates, we do not know with the same accuracy what its dimensions are. Those that we are using stem from the application of Newton's inverse-square law, which relates the mutual attraction of two objects to their masses and distance apart.

If we assume that the Earth's center of gravity is concentrated at the center of the Earth, then we can approximate g by learning how much the Earth's mass attracts a small, carefully calibrated mass taken to different parts of the globe. This procedure has been extensively used, and there is then the question of how much do local anomalies such as mountains affect the values we get. What we do find out from these studies is the amount of variation in gravity from one point to another. To get the average g for our Earth and from this derive the Earth's shape, we have to measure the values of gravity in every area in the world. Even with this information, some technical objections have been raised regarding the means of measurement.

One way to learn this elusive value over a considerable area is to observe the behavior of an Earth satellite. Being independent of local attritions, a freely flying satellite travels in its orbit under the action of only two factors, gravity and centrifugal force. Since we can determine the centrifugal force, the value of gravity can easily be derived. Once an acceptable value is found, we can compute the values of gravity for any place on the globe because we already know the local variations. With these data, we are ready to find the Earth's shape and learn its geography.

The *Project Vanguard* satellites are being launched on peace missions. The data they gather will be sent back to Earth for analysis by all scientists, independent of their citizenships. It is expected that the results of these analyses will be fully shared to promote further studies. This is the plan of the United States and of the International Geophysical Year Committee.

The military are co-operating on the *Vanguard* project. This is a seemingly odd turn of events. Here a proposition that shows promise of being the greatest peace offensive on Earth is being materially encouraged by a force whose historical objective has been destruction. Historically, too, military men have been loath to advise war unless they saw a good probability of winning it. Today, with the presence of nuclear weapons, intercontinental ballistic missiles, atomic submarines, and thousand-mile-per-hour airplanes, the military would find crystal-ball reading as good a method as any for determining the odds in winning a war.

What, then, are the reasons the military are backing something that appears to be a long way from bullets and bombs? The answer to this question lies in the modern modifier that has been given to warfare—*technological* warfare. The Air Force and Navy, for example, want their aircraft to go higher and faster. For this feat, the aircraft must be made of strong, heat-resistant materials. The development of such materials depends on the study of their molecular make-up. Taking a step further back, we see that we must first know the constituents of a molecule. The military are financing the learning of just such basic knowledge for the end purpose of better weapons.

From the military point of view, the satellites of *Project Vanguard* are simply instruments for basic research. The work would be sponsored whether or not an International Geophysical Year were approaching. Space flight is an ancillary thought.

We have to know many things before we can build higher-flying aircraft. We have to know the density of the air at the various altitudes, and from this information determine the drag of the hypothetical airplane, and, from this, the power required. The satellites will give us density values. We must know the effect of cosmic rays upon pilots. The satellites will give us data from which this information can be extracted. We must know the electron concentration in the ionosphere because this information will aid us in communications and missile guidance. For navigation purposes we would hold quite valuable a map of the jet streams in the higher altitudes. For even these data, the satellites can tell us. Thus, the military will be using *Project Vanguard* as a means to gather information for the more efficient preparation for a technological defense.

It is claimed that the country controlling an artificial satellite would have an overwhelming advantage over its enemy. It is extremely doubtful that this proposition could be true for the early satellites whose pay loads are so severely limited.

When larger satellites are built, and are able to hold and discharge defensive weapons and obtain data of immediate use, then the situation may change. But such military satellites, manned or unmanned, would not necessarily predicate military superiority. Present analyses seem to indicate a stalemate, although many authorities, such as Professor Oberth, disagree.

Proponents of the military-superiority thesis say that camera-bearing satellites will be able to keep a constantly open eye on enemy territories. These people reason that no major industrial activity, troop movements, preparations for air invasion, or other powerful military activities can be hidden from a system of Earth-circling satellites. This premise was true for the wars we have known, but would not necessarily hold true should a new one arise. Military tactics have changed. They have adapted themselves to atomic warfare and take into account the eventuality of intercontinental ballistic missiles. As a result, industry is being dispersed. If necessary, it can work underground, as it has done successfully in the past, and stay unobserved. Aircraft can take off from hidden bases. It is reported, for example, that the Scandinavians have built some of their runways inside of mountains. Aircraft can also take off when the sky is overcast, or at night, or when there is no satellite around to observe them. Troop movements can be made at night, though whether mass movements of troops will be necessary in a future war is questionable, since a concentration of troops would be an invitation for an atomic-bomb attack. Only for occupation do mass movements of men seem necessary, and for this maneuver we can presume that the enemy country is already on its knees and that its space weapons are either useless or nonexistent. Another logical countermeasure would be to misinform the satellites by letting them see mock-military projects.

What is involved in the use of satellites as platforms for launching atomic projectiles? There would be the problem of getting the projectiles from the Earth to the satellites. It does not seem feasible that an atomic weapon would be sent with only guidance equipment to carry it safely to altitude. This means a man must accompany the weapon. Such a pay load would require quite an advanced version of a cargo-carrying spaceship. Might it not be better to accomplish the military objective by using surface-to-surface missiles? These would be cheaper, could be fired at will, and would not have to wait upon favorable atmospheric conditions.

The answer, of course, is that ICBMs would have to be used. These are launched from permanent and expensive installations, the perfect target for any enemy. The problem then resolves itself into whether it is better to build cargo-carrying spaceships, or to build less vulnerable ICBM launching sites—or a number of each in accordance with past procedures.

Perhaps the larger satellites could be used for terminal or midcourse guiding of missiles. This presumes that the enemy has no satellites of its own to combat such weapon systems.

Measures, and countermeasures, and counter-countermeasures will be the story of the day should satellites be used for military purposes, and this is no different from current warfare except in sophistication. If one country is able to place an aggressive satellite in an orbit, it is probable that the enemy can send a weapon to the same altitude to destroy the vehicle.

The first thought would be to launch a small missile into the orbit of the enemy's satellite. Approaching from the opposite side of the globe and traveling toward the satellite, the missile would be exploded. The theory is that a cloud of shrapnel would be formed that would pierce the satellite several times a day forever. Many of us believed that this procedure was the answer, until it was remembered that even a mild explosion in the airless atmosphere would send the particles speeding in all directions. The probability of even one particle's remaining in the required orbit would be extremely remote.

Why not, then, launch the missile as the satellite was launched, taking care that the missile's fragments are projected tangent to the satellite's orbit? Being tangent to a satellite's orbit at a given point, even if we could manage to do this, is not the same as being in the satellite's orbit. As we know, an infinite number of ellipses can be drawn tangent to the same line at the same point. There is the rare possibility that the missile and the satellite might someday meet. This could easily be avoided because the country that can build a satellite for significant military purposes can also build a guidance system in it that can alter the vehicle's orbit out of harm's way.

At this point, the problem becomes almost entirely a logistic one. A rocket is sent up to home on and destroy a satellite. The satellite sends out jamming signals. Then a rocket is devised that is protected against jamming. The satellite is subsequently armed with a number of small missiles that can be used to destroy the rocket. The rocket in turn is armed with antisatellite missiles. This could go on and on, with the satellite's missile bearing a smaller missile called an anti-antisatellite missile, until logistics, cost, and common sense push over the concept.

Artificial satellites will probably never be used as direct military weapons. The fantastic cost and waste of making larger satellites expendable, the vast army of engineers and technicians needed to design, build and maintain them, and the great hazards involved in the precipitant launching of them, all cast grave doubts on their wartime value. Only as evidence of strength, could satellites win their case for peace.

8.   Space Satellites and You

The effects of space satellites upon each individual depend upon the development stage at which he sees them and the work he is doing. For scientists and engineers, the satellites will immediately exert a strong influence on their professional lives. Because of the opportunities for commercial exploitation, the later stages of satellite development will have meaning for most investors and industrialists. For the vast majority of people, satellites will not function directly in their daily lives until the vehicles reach one stage short of manned space flight. Still, the indirect influences of satellites at even their earliest stages will be felt by everyone.

Millions of dollars are being spent every year to improve materials for home and industry. These materials include such items as long-life and high-strength metals, temperature-resistant and moisture-resistant finishes, and rugged and reliable electronic elements. Vast sums are spent on test equipment that examine these materials for dependability and efficiency. Fatigue testers measure the life span of materials; hot and cold chambers measure the materials' resistance to temperature changes; humidity chambers show the effects of moisture; and atmospheric chambers contain mixed tests, including one for altitude effects.

In several of these tests, such as the temperature and altitude ones, extreme conditions are seldom reached. Yet it is these extreme conditions that are sometimes needed to discover a more efficient material for more moderate conditions. An artificial satellite lives in an environment of extreme conditions. It could almost be called a universal laboratory. For example, we can here run a life test even under the most adverse environmental circumstances. We have a large range of temperature conditions, some approaching close to absolute zero. We have an atmospheric chamber that none on Earth can match. From this laboratory can come near-perfect insulating materials for the homeowner, radio and television sets of much improved dependability, crashproof and lightweight metals and plastics for automobiles and aircraft, and probably the discovery of new materials.

The effects of an event are sometimes anticipated so strongly that they appear in our literature, education and philosophy decades before the event occurs. In literature, Jules Verne was probably the first man in modern times to give an account of space flight when he wrote about the trip of three men to the Moon. Today, space is virtually filled with space-flight characters. Their trips are followed and documented so precisely on radio and television programs that a stranger to our planet would be mystified to learn that we have never left our atmosphere.

The authors of most of these writings do considerable research before they venture off into space. They quite accurately depict the instrumentation needed, the power-plant requirements and operation, the natural phenomena that challenge the lives of spacemen, and the atmosphere and terrain of the planets they are visiting. On open questions, the authors and audience use their imaginations.

The literature about space is not restricted to radio, television, and technical reports. Books are being published giving presumably non-fiction accounts of the flights and landings of flying saucers peopled by creatures from outer space. Other books are being written contradicting the premises of these first books. Magazines are featuring the newest thoughts about rockets, satellites, and space flight. As the launching of the *Project Vanguard* satellites comes closer, we shall see even more emphasis being put on extra-Earth activities. The newspapers will be devoting more columns to the activities of the IGY committee and to their plans for upper-atmospheric research. Even the younger generation is being kept fully informed about space matters through the comic books and daily comic strips.

We can expect the literature dealing with space and space travel to grow almost as fast as our anticipations will grow when the first satellite is sent orbiting around the Moon. Only a few feet of bookshelves are needed now to house the published works dealing with the upper atmosphere and space. Shortly, entire library shelves and even sections will be necessary to hold just a sampling of the literary output. New novels will have their settings in astronautical laboratories, on manned satellites, and even on the Moon and Mars. The curious twist to us will be that the settings will most likely be treated quite subordinately. The concept of space travel will be no stranger than the concept of air travel.

When literature travels out of this world, education must follow. Our children instead of learning their addition tables by counting oranges and apples will be counting satellites and satelloids. Geography lessons will be illustrated by pictures of the Earth taken by cameras located at several hundred miles' altitude. No longer will we have to prove to our children that the Earth is round by asking them to observe the diminishing funnels of an ocean liner as it sails into the horizon. Unhappily, it has been the authors' experience during several such tests to see the ship, shortly after its sailing, become hidden by fog.

In the satellite's view of the Earth, clouds will generally be seen. These will have to be described and analyzed for the pupils. The cloud types will have to be identified as well as the mechanics of rain. The role of the Sun will have to be explained together with the formation and characteristics of the planets. At a young age, our children will be learning the rudiments of meteorology and astronomy.

Regardless of the teacher's fund of knowledge, his pupils will keep asking questions, some easy and some impossible. Why doesn't the satellite fall down? What's it made of? What's inside it? Why can't we see it in the daytime? Are there people in it? What do they do? Eventually, if only for self-preservation, teachers and parents will have to learn the answers. In this way, the effects of the new moons will be felt by even the most unscientific minded.

When the children reach high-school age, they will be assembling kits of model satellites designed by some enterprising manufacturers. Those builders able to incorporate instrumentation in their satellites will probably rise in the eyes of other model builders. We can anticipate contests in which accurate data-taking will be the goal. In this fashion, a new and vital prestige will be given to science as a lifework. To prepare for this, the students will demand of their schools and instructors more mathematics, more physics, more chemistry, and the addition of basic astronomy and meteorology to the curriculum. Because the satellite and its data are international, even the study of languages will increase. There will be no phase of science that will not have some of its branches reaching skyward, and have some young followers eager to climb them. The problem of the critical shortage of technical manpower in the United States may begin to dissolve in the first reflections from the orbiting vehicles.

Our step into space will be felt deep within our psyche. When a man climbs a high mountain and from its top sees beneath him the valleys and hills stretching into the distance, he experiences one of two emotions. He may see in his climb a conquering of the elements, a challenge that Nature accepted and lost. Despite his physical weariness, he will be a much stronger man than when he started on the expedition. From his height, he will be master of all he surveys, and to him the mountain will be likened to a footstool. This man believes that there is no world that cannot be won.

A second man can reach the mountaintop with far less strength than is in his body. He is overpowered by the mass and convolutions of the mountain, and shudders at the capriciousness of Nature. When he sees the depths of the gorges below, and feels the burning rays of the Sun through the clear atmosphere, and watches a distant cirrus cloud spiraling into the heavens, he is struck by his own littleness.

So, too, the satellite may give some people courage and others panic—courage to those who see the satellite as a mark of man's achievement, and panic to those who see the satellite as an effort wrought by all of man's genius but less than insignificant in the eyes of Nature.

The satellite will teach man many new values. He cannot watch the Earth spinning on its axis, see the continents shrunk to the size of small coins, look above the Earth's atmosphere and see countless stars in everlasting night, without asking himself fundamental questions. What is the meaning of life? Where do I fit into it? What part does religion play?

He might reappraise his lifework in the light of the contribution he is making to society. He might alter his notion of success. Looking through a cosmic scope, he might better judge the worth of money. He may consider his children not as the heirs of his life but rather as the genesis of a new one. Finally, he may turn more strongly to God and religion with admiration and gratitude.

It is fortunate that man's control over weather and climate is so small. Perhaps if he had more to say about the matter, he might find that in his greed he had eroded vast sections of the Earth's atmosphere. Still, man has never quite believed that he is not master of all he surveys. Even in ancient times, people were convinced that they could control the elements.

Many methods of affecting weather have been tried. One forthright approach was practiced in old Russia by a tribe that was not convinced that they were getting their fair share of rain. During a dry season, three priests would go to a sacred grove. Here they would climb a fir tree. One priest would beat on a kettle to imitate thunder, the second would wave two firebrands to imitate lightning, while the third would sprinkle the ground with water. If it still did not rain, the three priests were replaced.

Today we are told that if we cannot alter a situation, we must adapt ourselves to it. To be able to live to best advantage with weather we must be able to predict it. True, we know its general characteristics of coolness in the winter and warmness in the summer, which are described as climate, though even here we have seen in some parts of the world unorthodox changes. Still, the relative constancy of climate makes us particularly impatient with the vagaries of weather. Its influence not only on every business and profession but also on life is fundamental. Farmers, builders, shippers, pilots and investors carefully study the forecasts. It is a source of wonderment to the weathermen that the public has so much faith in predictions based only on minute studies of the global weather picture.

To arrive at an accurate forecast, meteorologists must know what is happening throughout the world's atmosphere. They must know the temperatures at the various layers, the pressures, humidities, winds, cloud formations, and many other factors that require hundreds of trained observers. To gain this information, men staff scores of weather stations and send balloon-borne instruments aloft to probe the atmosphere and radio back the data. These are plotted on charts and analyzed to form an instantaneous weather picture. In it, there are large open spaces owing to lack of observations over oceans and unpopulated areas. The picture is also distorted because the data are not taken simultaneously, and extrapolations must bridge the time gap. Knowing the immediate past history of some of the atmosphere and its probable present state, meteorologists make a prudent but far from infallible weather prediction.

To reconnoiter the weather most effectively, Dr. Harry Wexler of the United States Weather Bureau recommends that a satellite be placed in a 4,000-mile altitude orbit. This would give the satellite weather-observatory a four-hour period. From its height, the satellite would have an instantaneous field of view comparable in area to North America and its adjacent oceans, about the same area covered by a forecaster's working chart. Cloud areas and geographic features would be perceived. Also, a 4,000-mile satellite would have the same cloud system in view at least twice every 12-hour period, but the observatory would not move so quickly that individual cloud systems could not be distinguished and tracked. The satellite would have a westward component of travel in order for it to follow storm paths accurately, which have a west-to-east motion.

A satellite weather-observatory, even though unmanned, would shortly pay for itself, and the savings in life and property would be well worth the venture. Meteorologists would be able to tell us when a cyclone is brewing, what its path will be, and how much time there is for evacuation. Cyclonic storms tend to array themselves in a family extending from the southwest to the northeast. Fortunately for prediction, there is usually a known average spacing between these storms. If there is an unusually large space, then it is likely that a storm is being formed to fill the space, particularly if it occurs where the storm pattern has not yet reached maturity. Rain, snow, and other precipitation areas can be seen on a satellite radarscope. Even the altitude of the freezing level leaves its trace. These data would be telemetered to Earth for interpretation. It may even be that unusual weather is controlled by the Sun. We could soon find out by learning whether a correlation with solar radiations exist. Such a program could be extended to include long-range weather forecasting and predictions of climatic changes.

The proportion of sunlight that the Earth reflects is called the Earth's *albedo*. Variations in the Earth's climate have been related to changes in its albedo. Dr. Wexler estimates that a one per cent drop from the average albedo value of 35 per cent would lead to a world-wide warming of almost two degrees Fahrenheit. Since a large-scale cloudiness over the Earth would appreciably lower the Earth's reflectivity, clouds play an exceedingly vital part in our climate. A small change in the cloud density over the world could explain the drastic changes in the world's climate, which has ranged from extreme cold during the glacial period to the warmth of the later period. For accurate albedo studies, we could install in a satellite a number of photoelectric cells directed toward Earth. These would quickly tell us the albedo state we are in, and give us warning of changes.

Let us take a simple example and see how from small beginnings the man-made specks in the sky will affect ever widening circles of our economy.

Farm income from cotton and cotton seed is over $2 billion a year, which makes cotton the most valuable crop in the United States. To promote production, the weather must be quite co-operative. Just after a rainy period, planting must begin. During the early growing season, there must be sufficient moisture and sunshine to drive the cotton to maturity. As the season advances, the days must be dry ones else the cotton will rot. Six months after planting, the crop is harvested, almost entirely by hand.

During the cycle, the farmer's problems are these: if he waits too long before seeding, hoping for adequate rain, he may find himself in a summer drought. If the drought is protracted, then his irrigation system, if he has one, will be useless. As picking time nears, the farmer, now in fear of rain, studies every cloud in the sky, for if there is one chance shower, his crop grade is lowered. The stakes are a few days' extra growing time and a correspondingly greater yield against an inferior cotton. If rain is imminent, the farmer must hurriedly gather his pickers and ready his equipment for fast harvesting.

How much better and easier the task would be if he could really tell what kind of weather were scheduled! Some experts believe that such long-range weather forecasts will be possible, thus the farmer would know precisely when to plant and when to harvest. The pickers would know where and when to go for work. If a rainy summer were forecast, the farmer could use this knowledge to high advantage, perhaps by planting rice. The migrant pickers would be forewarned to look for other work. Manufacturers of cultivators, cotton pickers, cotton gins, and spinners would concentrate their production on other equipment. All this because meteorologists were analyzing data telemetered from Earth satellites and could tell what the weather would be.

The effects spread. Searching for a source of cotton, fabric manufacturers would begin bargaining for futures from the Soviet Union, Egypt, India, China, Brazil, and the West Indies. With the Soviet Union and China particularly, new trade agreements probably would have to be discussed. These could be reciprocal ones that could benefit all industry, or could cause knotty diplomatic problems.

Knowing that cotton supply was to be short and prices high, dress manufacturers would be planning their designs around synthetics and other fibers. This decision would affect the chemical plants that furnish the synthetics, and the mines that yield the raw materials, and the shops that service the miners. The circle widens. It touches hundreds of thousands of people. For the first time, though, any drastic effects can be ameliorated because there is ample time for planning.

Depending on weather analyses derived from the satellite will be hordes of office workers anticipating summer vacations. Looking forward to seeing these office workers will be the resort owners, and the airplane and steamship lines. It is easy to guess at the trend of prices and profits during the time a period of inclement weather is docketed. It is also easy to visualize the interplay of office politics when vacation schedules are being drawn.

It has been seriously suggested that we can change the course of some weather. In a novel scheme, the United States Weather Bureau is planning to use dry-ice seeding in an attempt to divert the paths of hurricanes. If the plan succeeds, then man will be able to steer hurricanes and other storms into areas where they can do little or no damage, such as over water or unpopulated areas. The theory was derived from the well-known rain-making experiments. Applied to hurricanes, seeding is expected to trigger an icing action in moisture-laden hurricane winds. Once started, the icing would spread throughout the hurricane, thereby creating a major heat unbalance. In this way, the energy balance in the area would be upset, in turn upsetting the natural path of the hurricane. If the theory works in test, then incipient storm areas such as those perceived by a weather-observing satellite could be destroyed while they are being born.

In our lifetimes we shall probably read reports from satellite weather stations. At that time, we shall certainly be accused of being old-fashioned should we ever be heard wondering what the weather will be like tomorrow.

Our crowded radio dial is known to all of us. It is most annoying when we are trying to separate one program from an encroaching one. Especially at night, when reception is good, unless we have a sharp-tuning receiver, we could easily find ourselves trying to unravel three superimposed broadcasts. In despair, we probably twist the dial to any other program merely because it is clear.

The problem of the crowded radio spectrum is worsening. More stations are demanding that the Federal Communications Commission assign them frequencies. As more frequencies are allocated, the stations move closer and closer together on the radio dial until saturation is approached. In some urban communities this point is being rapidly reached. It is true that expected technical developments will be able to squeeze more long-range broadcasting stations on the air. Still, the process cannot go on indefinitely.

There does exist a large frequency band not yet in extensive use —the *microwave band*. It lies in the region between the infrared waves and the short waves of radio. The military have been studying its characteristics, and every day are learning more about its properties. Radar, walkie-talkies, and automobile telephones all use part of the microwave band.

Microwaves have many of the characteristics of light. They travel in straight lines, can be reflected by electronic mirrors, and can be focused by electronic lenses. A microwave system which augments the company's cable network is being used by the telephone company to relay long-distance telephone conversations. Since these waves can travel only on line-of-sight paths, tall microwave towers spaced about 50 miles apart have been erected. The signals, such as a telephone conversation, are relayed from one tower to the next until the terminus is reached.

Suppose the towers were 200 miles high—several satellites, for instance. They could easily replace all the towers stringing across the United States. We could eliminate the expense of maintaining these towers and make unnecessary the erection of new ones. The power saving would be high. Compared with sending a message through a number of relay stations, or by successive reflections between the ionosphere and the Earth, as with long-wave radio signals, a microwave focused on a satellite and redirected to a receiver on Earth would consume only a tiny amount of power.

We are looking for an expansion of the commercial-broadcast band. A satellite could give such an expansion through the microwave band. The broadcasting station would send its program to the satellite, which would send it back to a tracking receiving station. If a 22,300-mile-high satellite were used, which is the one that appears stationary to an observer on Earth, then even tracking would not be needed. The program would then be relayed from the receiving station to the home radio sets. If such a microwave system were adopted, then we could be assured of at least a 100 per cent increase in the number of radio channels available.

The idea of using satellites as *repeaters* is not a new one. It has been proposed by many engineers including Bell Telephone Laboratory engineer Dr. J. R. Pierce. As a case in point, he takes the American Telephone & Telegraph Company and the British Post Office, who are co-operating in planning a transatlantic, 36-channel, two-way submarine telephone cable. These are not very many channels, especially for an estimated cost of $35 million. Pierce asks whether a channel 30 times as wide, one capable of carrying 1,080 telephone conversations or just one television program, would cost 30 times $35 million or about one billion dollars. Even if future cable developments could cut the costs of submarine cables, the savings would be small—unless the developments were spectacular. Since no one disputes the ability of an Earth satellite to relay communications, and since it is claimed that the first series of Earth satellites will cost only $35 million, would it not be wise to consider satellites rather than submarine cables for future transoceanic lines?

In the broadest sense, people are linked together through communications. Should there be faulty communications, misunderstanding and hardship would follow. Should there be a complete breakdown, it would not be long before chaos set in.

What elements comprise a near-perfect mass-communications system? We certainly would want our message or program material to be received by the widest possible audience—by the world. We would want the message transmitted economically, instantaneously and simultaneously. A system of Earth satellites could do even better. It could send not only a single program but also scores of programs at the speed of light to all parts of the world, and it could do the job at far less cost than we could attempt to do it with the means we have today. The only major ability that satellite communications would be lacking would be that of translating the programs into the tongues of the listeners.

Imagine the effects of world-wide freedom of communications wherein home stations could send their programs 12,000 miles as easily as 12 miles. Then any government desiring to keep its people ignorant would have to maintain a police force in comparison with which Hitler's Gestapo would seem as Boy Scouts. Counterbroadcasts would probably be used until finally there would arise a war of the air lanes.

The impact would be felt even before the first broadcasts hit the ether. Diplomats would ponder upon the probable effects of their opponent's propaganda. How would an enslaved people react if day after day they were to see the goods and services being offered and bought by the world's free people—the automobiles, refrigerators, clothes, foods and furniture? Certainly the volume and extensiveness of the program material would belie anyone's statement that these broadcasts had been devised purely for foreign consumption. It would be only a short time before the truth were known. What would be the effect if through television these people visited American factories, Scandinavian homes, German fairs, and French resorts —if they saw the roads and schools and theaters and farmlands— and the Easter parade on New York's Fifth Avenue, and on London's Bond Street? If they saw the free world?

Beyond the political effects would be the economic ones. Global advertising would be feasible. Vast new markets would be created by a newly informed world population. Small business and local commerce would be thrust into international markets. The effect of this revolution could create a standard of living and prosperity whose magnitude one could contemplate but would not dare predict. These international prospects for today's businesses are fully as probable as the national prospects were for American businesses 50 years ago.

Three or possibly four satellites spaced in an orbit 22,300 miles high could service every family in the world through radio communications. As we mentioned previously, the satellites would appear never to move, for their periods would be the same as the Earth's, 24 hours. If this altitude is too difficult for our present satellite-bearing rockets to reach, then nine satellites placed in a 257-mile-altitude orbit would suffice to ring the globe. World-wide radio coverage would still be assured, with the programs being relayed from one satellite to another until every receiving station was serviced.

When we have space satellites available for medical research, the study projects will be based on two phenomena that we do not have on Earth, the state of zero gravity, and the condition of unobstructed solar radiations. Biological and medical investigators will first ask how these factors affect elemental life. What happens to microorganisms living in a zero-gravity environment? Do they shrivel and die, grow to monster proportions, or behave "normally"? From the effects on microorganisms, we shall be able to extrapolate to the effects on larger organisms until we reach man. How do cosmic rays influence the growth and reproduction of vegetable life? The answer will tell us more about these strange rays and more about the constituents of vegetable life.

Chlorella algae, when exposed to sunlight, produces, in one hour, 50 times its own volume in oxygen, when sunlight is measured at ground level. How would the algae react if it were exposed to the full spectrum of the Sun? If the algae's oxygen output were increased, in accordance with the doubling of the solar constant, then its growth might correspondingly increase. This could lead to the accelerated growing of plant life and food in space. If these plants could be raised through hydroponic gardening, then the world might someday have farms 1,000 miles above the Earth.

Space offers an unequaled laboratory for the discovery of new medicants. To work with, the researchers would have a near-perfect vacuum, a wide temperature range going down to nearly absolute zero, a zero-gravity state, and an open Sun. One example of the type of studies that could be made is derived from work with mutant strains. We may remember from our biology that the cells in our bodies contain *genes* which, arrayed in single file, comprise threadlike chains called *chromosomes*. It is believed that the genes determine the physical and mental characteristics of man. Each of the genes passed on during conception is said to determine a unique characteristic of the offspring, such as color of hair, color of eyes, bone structure, and mental capacity. When a gene is missing or changed, the characteristic associated with it is changed.

Occasionally, an individual is born having a strikingly unusual characteristic. In man, the change may be that of webbed hands or hemophilia (bleeding). If this characteristic is inheritable, it is called a *mutation*. It may be one of two types, that caused by changes in the chromosome, or by changes in the gene structure. To the individuals involved, most mutations are harmful. But mutations in

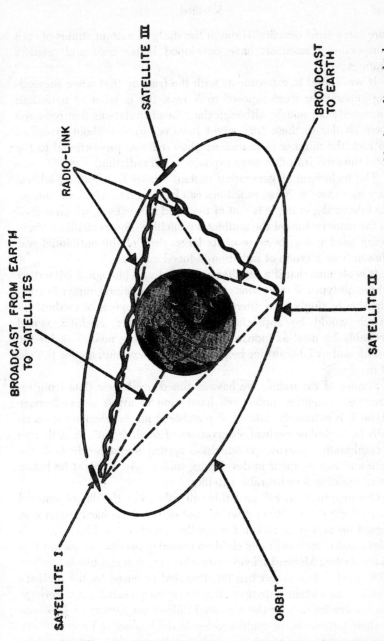

Three or possibly four satellites orbiting around the Earth at 22,300 miles could relay radio and television programs from any part of the globe to any other part.

rare cases yield benefits. Through the study of mutant strains of corn and oranges, scientists have developed better corn and seedless oranges.

It was found in experiments with the fruit fly that when succeeding generations were exposed to X rays, the number of mutations increased enormously, although the type of mutations that occurred were similar to those that might have occurred without exposure. In fact, the number of mutations observed was proportional to the total time the fruit flies were exposed to the radiation.

The technique of generating mutant strains by exposing laboratory specimens to X-ray radiations can be turned to man's advantage. An interesting example is that of the mold *Penicillium,* which is used in the manufacture of the antibiotic penicillin. The Penicillium strain being used today, because of its large yield of the antibiotic, was chosen from a group of radiation-induced mutants.

It is obvious that if a satellite were used as a biological laboratory where all types of radiations could easily be obtained, either in combination or singly by a filtering process, the progress of medical research would be appreciably increased. Later satellites would probably be used as industrial plants producing medicines for the world, and as laboratories helping discover new mutants for the aid of mankind.

Studies of the nature we have outlined need their data from recoverable satellites, unless we have time to await manned space flight. It is extremely difficult, if possible at all, to telemeter successfully biological or medical observations of small organisms. Although a combination microscope-television system might be devised, the time and money spent in developing such a system might be better spent building a recoverable satellite.

Our imaginations will probably run wild when the day of manned space flight dawns. Even if we are not one of those hardy souls who signed up at a planetarium for the first flight to the Moon, we still might find ourselves or our children someday needing to ascend to a space station. Medical science may discover, as it did to some extent with X rays, that cancer can be alleviated or cured by the patient's exposure to certain radiations, maybe primary cosmic rays. Perhaps the ultraviolet rays of the Sun could affect the course of leukemia or rheumatic fever, or could accelerate the healing of broken bones. One strong possibility for the cardiac patient is that under a condition of zero gravity the strain on his heart could be decreased because his weight would be eliminated. How to get the patient to the space station without overstraining his heart is another problem.

It is an expected and verified experience that as the temperature of a metal is reduced, electrical current is able to flow somewhat more freely through it. A most odd phenomenon occurs when the temperature of certain metals is brought close to absolute zero. Lead, for example, behaves quite normally out of the range of absolute zero. Its resistance to electrical current decreases smoothly according to law and is easily measured down to 7.2 degrees absolute, its *critical temperature*. However at this temperature the metal's resistance drops precipitously to a barely measurable value about one trillionth its room-temperature value. So low is this resistance that here something like perpetual motion is in sight. Experiments have shown that a ring formed of lead will support for months an electrical current that has been induced by a single pass of a magnet through the ring's center. This characteristic is called *supraconductivity*.

Not all metals have been made to exhibit supraconductivity. On the idea that the purity of a metal had something to do with the effect, gold was tested. Unhappily for the proposed theory, this noble metal showed no sign of supraconductivity, whereas the relatively impure tin and lead did. Why supraconductivity occurs is unexplained, and why it starts at a definite and fixed temperature for those elements that respond is also a mystery. Here is a problem that could be studied in a satellite, for in this vehicle there would be a near-perfect cold chamber. If the chamber could be insulated from the Sun's radiant energy and the Earth's reflected energy, then within the chamber the temperature could easily be brought quite close to absolute zero. Even if the insulation were not adequate, it would not take much power to drive the temperature down. For low-temperature investigations, experimenters are used to receiving telemetered data, and therefore a satellite laboratory would not require physicists to change many of their techniques. Added to the study of the electrical resistance of metals at depressed temperatures would be studies of other circuit elements such as condensers and coils.

One possible result of this research would be the design and regulation of electrical circuits by temperature, which could be done when circuits are operating near absolute zero. To decrease current flow, we simply raise the ambient temperature; to cut the circuit off, we raise the temperature further. One cannot help wonder what the characteristics of a complex circuit would be when operating under supraconductive conditions. From the answers, we can certainly expect more understanding of the associated phenomena of magnetism and heat. With this understanding will come much-improved equipment.

There are occasions in the life of a society when a radical invention basically changes the values, beliefs, and behavior of its members. The invention of printing was one such event, radio a second, and the automobile a third. Social scientists have speculated on how a radical invention is accepted, altered, or rejected depending on the ability of people to blend the invention into their own values, beliefs, and physical behavior. The social scientists also have disjointed and partial studies on aspects of these processes as they occur in our society and in less complex ones. But these investigators have never had the chance to make a systematic series of studies in depth and over a period of time both preceding and succeeding the radical invention.

The announcement of plans to launch the first Earth satellites has given the social scientists an opportunity to begin a series of unparalleled studies. Dr. Donald N. Michael of the National Science Foundation, formerly a physicist and now a social psychologist and research consultant, has proposed a comprehensive program for such social research. He says that "we have the opportunity to follow the evolution of behavior, values, and beliefs as they change into new species, or become extinct, under the influences of technical modifications, for example, the unmanned satellite becoming the manned one. We can study this evolution as it occurs. And possibly, most important of all, we can for the first time in history do detailed studies on the states of mind, values and fantasies of people *before* they are exposed to a new development as well as after. Thus we can get that first half of a before-after research design so crucial to hypothesis testing in all fields, and so especially difficult to realize in the area of social change."

Clearly such a continuing series of studies would make significant contributions not only to our understanding of the dynamics of social change but also to our application of social science. The overriding purpose of the program would be to use the results of these studies as a means for devising better theories, new methods, and new hypotheses for understanding the ways societies change.

What change takes place in the understanding of certain concepts as they become part of the thinking of at least broad sections of the public when the man-in-space becomes more and more part of commonplace life? Such concepts that will be affected are gravity, centrifugal force, the "vacuum" between planets, weightlessness, radiations from the Sun and from space, rocket engines, rocket propellants, astral navigations, and the physical and psychological attributes that astronauts must possess. Here a fascinating folklore may evolve.

And finally, what are the consequences of the people's understanding? Does it simplify or complicate their picture of the world and their place in it? What are the present fantasies and expectations of people, concerning the accomplishments and especially the consequences of the satellite launchings? How will these be modified as the broadside of facts and fancy increases? How are later patterns of fact and fantasy related to the present patterns?

Not in the very near future, but certainly not in a distant one, when space flight is a reality, the Internal Revenue Service will have an unusual question to answer. Can the United States collect income tax from a man who spends most of his time out of this world?

The satellite might even intrude into the lovers' corner. On nights when the Moon is hidden by the shadow of the earth, couples will still be able to gaze skyward and, with the aid of binoculars, look fondly at an artificial Moon. Whether the need for binoculars will dim the couple's ardor is not for the authors to decide.

9.   International Geophysical Year

The Earth has existed for about three billion years. Man has been here a million of them, yet until recently he has had only a fuzzy idea of the globe he inhabits. It is a dynamic globe spinning on its axis 1,000 miles an hour at the equator, racing around the Sun 67,000 miles an hour, and orbiting on the fringe of our star galaxy 175 miles a second—all these motions occurring on the backdrop of an expanding universe.

With a universe to explore, what has man accomplished? He has dug a four-mile well in California, though the Earth goes down 4,000 miles. He has flown 17 miles high, though the atmosphere extends 600 miles up and interstellar distances are measured in light years. Thus, man's present physical frontiers can be wholly encompassed in a spherical shell 21 miles thick. These frontiers will be pushed back during 1957–1958 when the Earth undergoes the most intensive study it has ever received. For this purpose, artificial satellites will be used as probing instruments.

Even an approximate investigation of our world is a gigantic undertaking. It requires that scientists and laboratories be placed at all physically significant points on our globe, and that these locations have facilities adequately instrumented and financed. To obtain scientific data about our Earth, devoted workers taking thousands of detailed readings of scores of natural occurrences will be needed. Even this fulfillment may not be enough. Take any atmospheric phenomenon such as a magnetic storm. How does it grow, reach a maximum and then decrease? What is its global distribution? For answers, scientists must make many simultaneous observations. A specified period must be set aside when an entire technical community concentrates only on this one phenomenon. In this manner, its characteristics can be closely described and can yield a pattern of behavior for other phenomena.

The world's solution to the problem is the IGY. Here we have a fixed time interval designated for intensive study of the Earth and its environment. Instruments are to be sent several hundred miles into the sky to test the atmosphere, and satellites are to be launched on 18,000-mile-per-hour orbits around the Earth. Expeditions are going to almost inaccessible locations in the Arctic and the Antarctic. World-wide periods of emergency studies within the IGY are being anticipated and arranged.

International co-operation for learning more about our natural environment is not new. The first *International Polar Year* was held in 1882 when meteorological, magnetic and auroral stations were established in the arctic regions. This pioneering work disclosed how the northern auroras were distributed at the geomagnetic pole. To this day, the data obtained at that time remain useful in the studies of the Earth's magnetism.

In 1932, fifty years later, a *Second International Polar Year* was held. Here again, many nations collaborated in making geophysical measurements in the north polar regions. Probably the most important contribution to this effort was an increase in understanding the ionosphere. This knowledge greatly advanced the science of radio communications.

Acting in view of these precedents, scientists urged that a third international effort in geophysics be undertaken. The period from July 1, 1957, to December 31, 1958, was chosen because this interval corresponds with that of major solar activity. The proposed United States program for the IGY surpasses in scope and geographical coverage the earlier international programs, which were largely limited to the north polar regions.

The scientists have made their programing flexible. This permits intensified observations during times of especially remarkable solar or other activities. There are four types of intervals when emergency observation programs may be scheduled within the IGY. These are classified as *Regular World Days, Alerts, Special World Intervals,* and *World Meteorological Intervals.*

The Regular World Days comprise several days per month. Two consecutive days are designated at new moon, and the other days near quarter phase and prominent meteor showers. When there is an unusually active solar region in the Sun's disk, a world-wide Alert will be broadcast. This will remain in effect until the activity subsides or until the region passes out of sight. The Alert will also serve notice that the probability of solar flares is heightened, warning that there is a strong possibility that geomagnetic disturbances will follow, and that a Special World Interval will be invoked. Special World Intervals are to be called on 24-hour notice at times when a significant geomagnetic disturbance may begin. The interval will end if the forecast disturbance does not materialize, or when the disturbance has subsided. The World Meteorological Intervals comprise a series of ten consecutive days each quarter year. These periods include the times of seasonal changes, and also three Regular World Days.

The communication networks for distributing notices of Alerts and Special World Intervals are centered at the National Bureau of Standards at Fort Belvoir, Virginia, and at Anchorage, Alaska. It is planned to broadcast the IGY information on standard-frequency stations. The present arrangements for international meteorological data interchange are expected to continue, which include a daily interchange with Europe and Japan. Weekly reports will also be available, which will give detailed information about ground observations of solar activity, geomagnetism and other phenomena.

Geophysics is the study of the solid Earth, its seas and its atmosphere. It has played a leading part among the sciences in directing man's thoughts and work toward understanding his world. For experience and techniques, the study has drawn upon many other studies and has fathered still more. It includes subjects such as meteorology, oceanography and vulcanology, all of which tell about the Earth's atmosphere, crust and interior. Extraordinary relationships among the various disciplines are often uncovered, such as those existing between oceanography and vulcanology and between geomagnetism and the ionosphere. Beyond the known relationships are others that are suspected but not proved, and probably many that are not even suspected.

Geophysics has not only given us theory but also practical results. From surveys of the Earth's geomagnetic and gravitational fields we have learned the location of deeply buried oil and coal resources, and of mineral deposits. Navigation of ships and aircraft has been simplified through accurate mapping of the magnetic fields in the trade routes. More effective radio communications have arisen out of fundamental studies of the ionosphere, and recently the theory of *whistlers* (odd whistling notes heard below the normal-broadcast band), gained through observations of atmospheric lightning, promise data that could affect our concept of the height of the atmosphere and of the content of space immediately surrounding it.

There is no natural phenomenon that the geophysicist does not want to study synoptically and extrapolate to its origin. When the nuclear physicists describe the action of radiations upon our atmosphere, the geophysicists ask how these rays are distributed and what their origin is. When ionospheric storms pass through our atmosphere and radios fade out, the geophysicists want to relate the disturbances to the Sun or to the newly discovered *radio stars*, the stars that emit radio-frequency waves. When meteorologists give a weather picture and nature whips up violent hurricanes, geophysicists seek the global picture and the natural forces that created it.

The goal of geophysics is to give us a generalized description of our natural environment so that we can understand and predict its changes over a span of time. IGY committee member L. V. Berkner points out that the Earth's major surface features change so slowly that we may travel from place to place to study them, and still have the leisure of ages to analyze them. Other features such as the level of the seas or the magnitude of the glaciers change relatively fast. Yet time in man's mind is so short that each generation can make "epochal" observations to learn the nature of these changes. Because these epochal bench marks are not apt to give man immediate benefits, however important the information may be to his progeny, he has been passive about establishing them. Yet how quickly modern scientists have made use of records handed down to them. How eagerly these men study the few notes left by Henry Hudson, who in the early sixteenth century sailed the *Half Moon* into the great bay in Canada named after him. He stood on the shore to record the event on the stone of a giant cliff rising out of the bay, and over the intervening years, his mark has risen 60 feet above the water. This record tells us the rate of rise of the northern end of our continent as it recovers from the glacial loading of the Pleistocene epoch.

A few aspects of our environment change quickly and noticeably, items such as the weather, and the tides in the air and sea.

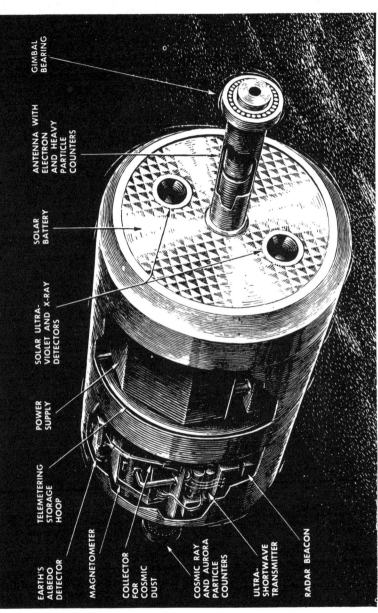

GIMBAL BEARING

ANTENNA WITH ELECTRON AND HEAVY PARTICLE COUNTERS

SOLAR BATTERY

SOLAR ULTRA-VIOLET AND X-RAY DETECTORS

POWER SUPPLY

TELEMETERING STORAGE HOOP

EARTH'S ALBEDO DETECTOR

MAGNETOMETER

COLLECTOR FOR COSMIC DUST

COSMIC RAY AND AURORA PARTICLE COUNTERS

ULTRA-SHORTWAVE TRANSMITTER

RADAR BEACON

One suggested artificial satellite is Dr. S. F. Singer's *Mouse*, a small instrumented cylinder intended for a pole-to-pole orbit. (*Sperryscope*)

Great rainstorms, for example, occur rapidly and at irregular intervals. Though often arising unannounced, they have a strong bearing on human behavior and existence. From the storms, meteorologists learn about the make-up of our atmosphere. Knowing patterns of events such as these extends the control we have over nature's organization.

Several years in advance of the IGY, the USNC-IGY (United States National Committee for the IGY) started working on various scientific aspects of the program. In the middle of 1955, because of the government's support of the program, the initial studies of the special "satellite" group became increasingly important. It was then that a USNC-IGY Technical Panel on the Earth Satellite Program was formed. The functions of the panel are to develop, co-ordinate and direct the over-all scientific satellite effort. The panel's members were chosen from among the country's most distinguished scientists.

There are 13 USNC-IGY Technical Panels. Together with the Earth Satellite Panel, these comprise Aurora & Airglow, Cosmic Rays, Geomagnetism, Glaciology, Ionosphere, Longitude & Latitude, Meteorology, Oceanography, Rocketry, Seismology & Gravity, Solar Activity, and World Days & Communications. Except for the panel on World Days & Communications, the panels on Rocketry and on Earth Satellites are the only ones that are devoted to the means of accomplishing a study rather than to a study itself—the Aurora & Airglow Panel are to investigate a definite physical phenomenon, as are the panels on Cosmic Rays, Geomagnetism, and so forth. The three exceptional panels are service ones, owing duty to all the disciplines. There is not one study on the IGY agenda to which rockets and satellites cannot give useful data. For example, to seismological studies the IGY scientists have linked gravity, whose value the satellites are being instrumented to determine. The IGY will be the world's first practical use of orbital vehicles, and the first international use of rockets for co-operative scientific research. Without these instruments, the IGY program would be gravely curtailed.

Rockets will help us explore the field of solar-terrestrial relationships. Although we know the character of solar radiations at the bottom of the atmosphere, we are not so sure about the situation in the upper atmosphere. Ground-based measurements, for example, do not tell us which solar radiations are responsible for producing the different ionospheric layers. Speculations about solar-flare radiations causing sudden ionospheric disturbance fill many volumes, yet the answer may be furnished during one rocket flight. The entire problem of determining an adequate solar index for effects such as solar-weather dependencies, geomagnetic disturbances and cosmic-ray increases seems almost totally dependent upon measurements made from rockets.

The relationships between the aurora, ionospheric currents, high altitude winds, and fluctuations in the Earth's magnetic field are still to be clarified. For a full understanding of the energy balance and dynamic conditions within the high atmosphere, one must know at what levels, in what quantities, and in what spectral regions energy is absorbed or radiated. The relation of high-altitude phenomena to low-altitude meteorology is an open question.

These indicate only a few of the many complex problems relating to the high atmosphere. A fundamental purpose of the rocket IGY program is to shed light upon the solutions. Basic meteorological data will be obtained at new locations and at various times by using established rocket techniques; the variables measured will be pressure, temperature, density, and winds. The chemical and ionic composition of the high atmosphere will be found. Emphasis will be placed on learning the nature of the ions at the various ionospheric levels, as this information is vital for developing ionospheric theory. The vertical distribution of ozone, and the question of the presence of nitrous oxide and water vapor in the high atmosphere will be subjects of extensive studies. There will be measurements of air fluorescence and determinations of the heights and intensities of day-glow radiations. The solar spectrum in the ultraviolet and X-ray regions will be learned by means of photon counters, with special attention being given during solar flares.

Rockets make possible the direct measurements of quantities that are either not observable or are only indirectly observable from the ground. The vehicles can also be used for measuring the altitude dependence of geophysical parameters. But they have a marked disadvantage in that they can spend little time at any one altitude during their flight, and that their total flight time is relatively short. Particularly in the case of the large rockets used for extreme-altitude studies, the vehicles are not easily adapted to synoptic or long-term studies. This is an unfortunate shortcoming, since fluctuations in solar effects such as ultraviolet and X-ray radiations, cosmic-ray intensities, current rings encircling the Earth, and particle streams impinging upon the high atmosphere are among the most important and interesting problems connected with the physics of the upper atmosphere and with solar-terrestrial relationships.

An Earth-circling satellite makes it possible to prescribe long-term observations. It is planned to use the IGY satellites for the following types of experiments, the number being carried out depending on the total pay-load capacity of the vehicles launched:

(a) Determination of outer atmospheric densities by observing the air-drag effect upon the satellite's orbit.

(b) Obtaining more accurate measures of the Earth's equatorial radius and oblateness, of intercontinental distances, and of other geodetic data.

(c) Long-term observations of solar ultraviolet radiation.

(d) Studies of intensities and fluctuations in intensity of the cosmic and other particle radiations impinging upon the outer atmosphere.

(e) Determination of the density of hydrogen atoms and ions in interplanetary space.

(f) Observations of the Chapman-Störmer current ring.

(g) If possible, determination of the distribution of mass in the Earth's crust along the orbital track.

The atmosphere is the working fluid of an enormous heat engine driven by the Sun. Large- and small-scale circulation systems transport heat from the tropics to the polar regions, thereby bringing storms and cold to one area and compensating at perhaps the other side of the globe. Growth of knowledge of basic weather patterns will be greatly facilitated in the IGY by the planned global network of surface and altitude stations making weather observations, and especially by the pole-to-pole lines of upper-air meteorological stations. Regular soundings to an anticipated height of 20 miles will be particularly important in revealing the three-dimensional structure of the atmosphere.

IGY scientists will have one significant advantage over previous observers in the field of meteorology—simultaneity of world-wide observations covering a period of sufficient length to allow reasonable completeness in the study of man's physical environment. The

United States program in meteorology is designed primarily to increase knowledge of the structure and motions of the atmosphere. Complete understanding of the zonal and meridional flow patterns in the atmosphere requires better information about the intensity and mode of exchange of energy, momentum, water vapor, and mass flow between tropics and polar regions, between troposphere and stratosphere, and between Northern and Southern Hemispheres.

Over-all solar activity grows and subsides alternately in about 11 years—the sun-spot cycle. Individually active areas on the Sun show cycles varying from a few minutes up to several months or more. These variations are clearly associated with terrestrial phenomena. As 1957–1958 will be a period of maximum solar activity, IGY scientists will develop detailed and comprehensive records in this field by means of systematic observations of the Sun through improved and faster co-ordination of the observing programs of the solar observatories of the world. Solar activity will be observed in the visible spectrum and at radio frequencies. In particular, solar flares will be studied and correlated with changes in cosmic rays, ionospheric and auroral disturbances, and geomagnetic phenomena. Other essential parts of the program will include observations of sun spots, solar magnetic fields, and line profiles of flares.

Modern civilization, being highly dependent on reliable transportation and communication, requires a knowledge of natural events that might cause interference. For some radio technicians, especially those engaged in radio aircraft navigation, the need for such knowledge goes beyond the consideration of economics, sometimes reaching the level of life-or-death importance. Predicted disturbances in communications can often be avoided or circumvented, but when information concerning these disturbances is lacking or inadequate, disasters may occur.

Even today a man standing on his back porch in Seattle, watching the play of the aurora borealis, enjoys the spectacle and scarcely realizes that a pilot flying across the North Atlantic may be in serious trouble because of the aurora's interference with the functioning of his radio set.

A spectroscopic observation program during auroral displays will give the distribution, geographically and with respect to time, of radiations of the auroral spectrum. The visual and photographic observations of the aurora have as a goal the drawing of synoptic maps showing aurora distribution at small intervals, and the collection of data for statistical studies of aurora correlated with other geophysical phenomena and with solar phenomena. Visual and photographic observations will give a general picture of the visual aurora, and radar will provide a record of the ionization associated with the aurora. As the terminal end of the path of ionized particles from the Sun and the only portion of that path that is visible, the aurora enables theoretical geophysicists to study this stream of particles, its path through space, its capture in the equatorial ring, and its subsequent bombardment of the atmosphere about 23 degrees from the magnetic poles. With modern techniques, the IGY scientists will fill the gaps in knowledge about the aurora borealis in the Arctic, gather data previously unavailable about the aurora australis in the Antarctic, and trace the relationship between the two.

The scientists also expect to learn why there are large decreases in cosmic-ray intensity during some magnetic storms, and the reasons behind the fluctuations in cosmic-ray intensity near sun-spot maximum, the world-wide variation of cosmic-ray intensity with the sunspot cycle, and the sudden large increase of cosmic-ray intensity within an hour or less after the beginning of solar flares. Observers working at a network of stations will derive their data from simultaneous balloon and rocket flights in different latitudes and longitudes during periods of increased solar activity. Although restricted in longitude, the satellites will contribute much data to the high-altitude synoptic picture.

The ionosphere, the region of rarefied ionized gas between 50 and 250 miles above the Earth, is studied chiefly by means of radio waves. Vertical-incidence soundings, in which radio waves are bounced off the ionosphere back to the station of origin, reveal the height of the layers and of the *critical radio frequencies*, those that pass through the ionosphere and those that are reflected back to the Earth. By means of these studies, scientists can predict radio blackouts near those areas where a network of ionospheric sounding stations exists, but major gaps of interest to the United States lie in the Arctic, South America, Antarctic, Equatorial Pacific, and North Atlantic, as well as elsewhere in the world.

Variations in the Earth's magnetism can be traced to two different causes: those occurring slowly over long periods of time and resulting from changes in the interior or in the crust of the Earth, and those happening rapidly and coming from influences high over the Earth's surface, either in the upper atmosphere or even above it. The geomagnetic program consists of a series of experiments designed to yield facts about the rapid magnetic-field fluctuations, which are usually accompanied by disturbances in radio-wave propagation and often by auroral displays, and which also increase in number and intensity with an increase in the number of sun spots. The demonstration of the existence of great electrical currents, measured in hundreds of thousands of amperes and flowing in the upper atmosphere, their nature, and their cause will also be part of the over-all program.

When man steered his ship only by the stars, he was not exempt from difficulties inherent in the unknown motions of the physical aspects of his world. Storms might drive him off course and obscure the signposts needed for his navigational technique, the stars, while strange currents and unexpected calms could become disastrous to him, both directly and indirectly in their effects on the weather that surrounded him. The shifting of the latitude and longitude as he sailed on must have disturbed all his calculations based on the positions of the stars. Observations for the more precise determination of longitudes and latitudes will be made at 20 IGY stations around the world. Astronomical longitudes and latitudes are obtained by observing the positions of celestial bodies with respect to the plumb line, or the direction of gravity. Satellites will be used to determine more accurately the magnitude and direction of gravity. Thus, in the finding of the differential shifts between continents, the values of the co-ordinates for each station will be learned with only small errors. A comparison of these values with others to be obtained in the future will enable scientists to determine by what amounts, if any, the continents are shifting with respect to each other.

In the related Moon-position program, the scientists will try to solve several special problems in astronomy, geophysics, physics, and geodesy concerning uniform time, the irregular rotation of the Earth, and the size and shape of the Earth. Mean solar time (universal time) is known to be nonuniform because of variations in the rotation of the Earth. Time based on the orbital motion of the Moon (ephemeris time) will be determined with great accuracy and used to obtain information about the irregular changes in the speed of rotation of the Earth.

Although gravity measurements are made by many nations, there exists no universally accepted standard. The IGY committee will in-augurate a program of extension of the world gravity network to those areas difficult to reach, and will attempt to resolve differences in observational values in regions already surveyed. Knowledge of the Earth's true shape depends on better data on the direction and strength of the pull of the Earth, the intensity of the gravity field, and the direction of the plumb line. Small details of departure from average conditions, such as those used in gravity prospecting for minerals and petroleum, and larger and more extensive departures or anomalies of regional character, influence the precision of astronomi-cal measurements and of measurements involved in the laying of the basic network for air maps. The United States plans a number of gravitational studies for the IGY. Gravimeter measurements are to be co-ordinated with the seismic exploration program and are to be carried out by the same personnel. The great gap in the international network of gravity observations now extending over most of the Southern Hemisphere will be filled, thereby supplying the means for drawing reliable base maps of the whole world.

Although man seems helpless where such physical events as earth-quakes are concerned, actually he can minimize the effects of these disasters by improving his knowledge of their nature, and by deter-mining the likelihood of their occurrence and extensiveness. Seis-mological observations and measurements have long been conducted on an internationally co-operative basis. The IGY will permit addi-tional measurements in remote areas, particularly in the Antarctic and the equatorial Pacific islands.

Some of the largest earthquakes have occurred in the sub-Antarctic region, and earthquakes are occurring on the Antarctic Continent itself, but little is known of the regional seismicity or liability to earth-quakes of the various parts of the Antarctic Continent.

At the stationary centers, geophysicists will study the Earth's deeper structure and the locations of any earthquake rifts or zones of instability that may occur in the Antarctic Continent. The work of these stations will be co-ordinated with that of an international network including special installations in other parts of the Earth for the study of the Earth's crust and of the deep interior. A further study of strain accumulation in the Earth which leads to danger of earthquakes will provide a possible approach to earthquake fore-casting, and there will be an investigation of the accumulation of strain in the solid Earth under the pull of the Sun and the Moon.

The winds and weather of the world play across a surface that is approximately three-fourths water. And the currents of the oceans move constantly in a huge circulatory system that vitally affects the climates of the one fourth of the Earth that is land. A study of motions of the deep currents in the sea, such as the vast exchange of polar water masses with those of warmer oceans, is a requisite of long-range weather forecasting. Changes of sea level and tidal phenomena provide information about currents and geomagnetic effects and give important indications of significant weather trends, such as periods of gradual warming up of the entire world.

The over-all objective of the island observatories project is to obtain an understanding of sea-level changes of both short and long periods and their relationship to other phenomena in the ocean and the atmosphere. Oscillations in sea level are related to atmospheric disturbances, storm waves, high-altitude jet streams in the atmosphere, and a heavy surf of unknown origin. Seasonal changes in sea level may be due to large-scale flow of water masses or to storage of water by the continents. Data will be collected at 30 stations, located principally on islands.

One effect of the warming up of the entire Earth would be the gradual melting of the world's supply of frozen water, the great glaciers and polar icecaps. If continued over a long period of time, this would have tremendous effects on the economic and political events in the world, including the opening of presently ice-locked ports in the far north, submersion of important coastal cities and low-lying coastal lands, and alterations in the distribution of vast arid and verdant areas.

Glaciers are found on all continents except Australia and occur in the tropics, in South America, Africa, and New Guinea. About 10 per cent of the Earth's land surface is now covered by ice.

Glaciers are extremely sensitive to meteorological factors, and in their variations indicate climatic changes of the past which in some instances can be dated by geologists and botanists. The stratigraphy and thermal condition of a glacier also reveal evidence of present and past climate. In turn, glaciers, particularly the two existing ice sheets in Greenland and Antarctica, exert an appreciable effect on the weather of the planet.

The study of the glaciers of the world, an assessment of their present status, and an examination of their delicate relationship with existing climate will occupy the glaciologists. The IGY program will encompass detailed studies at points in the Northern Hemisphere and at stations in the Antarctic, as well as reconnaissance observations in western United States, Alaska, and portions of the Arctic in co-operation with Denmark and Canada. Observations made at Antarctic stations and by traverse parties operating between stations and radiating outward from them will have as main objectives studies of the present condition of the Antarctic ice sheet with regard to nourishment, wastage, volume and extent, structure, thermal condition, and variations.

With the close of the International Geophysical Year 1957–1958, we shall see the close of the first use of artificial Earth satellites. In their use, we shall have witnessed not only many scientific advances and tremendous public interest but also strong international co-operation.

In its hunger for more data and for industrial use of satellites, the world will want larger and larger orbiting vehicles. It will demand that they go higher into the atmosphere and farther into space as advanced scouts of the Earth. Among the proposed projects there will be those demanding that the satellites be recoverable on Earth, and that they bring back from their travels information that can be examined and sorted first-hand. It will not be too long before man will want to populate the space vehicles and pilot them to landings on the Moon and nearby planets.

10. Mice and Monkeys—Then Men

As we learn to master the techniques of launching satellites of larger sizes, we shall quickly reach the point where we want to put more than spectrometers and cloud chambers and magnetometers into them. After all, our goal is manned space flight. In the beginning, our laboratory-type experiments will follow the classical pattern, the use of mice and monkeys.

When scientists first decided to experiment with upper-atmospheric animal-carrying vehicles, aeromedical experts had already gathered a substantial amount of experience in their laboratories about the behavior of animals in a near vacuum. The results of such studies, as reported by Fred A. Hitchcock, of Ohio State University, indicate the need for a close-to-perfect pressurization system for any animal headed for the upper atmosphere or space.

Immediately following exposure to a near vacuum, a research animal's respiration becomes deep and rapid. This condition lasts for a matter of seconds. Marked abdominal distension occurs immediately, due to the expansion of gases present in the intestinal tract. The animal collapses in about eight seconds. Mild convulsions generally occur in from 10 to 12 seconds and last for several seconds. Following this the animal is quiescent except for occasional respiratory gasps, which are ineffective in ventilating the lungs. Usually lacrimation, salivation and urination occur. Thirty to forty seconds following the reduction of pressure, a secondary swelling begins. This swelling usually first occurs in the hind limbs and lower abdomen, and progresses headward.

According to Hitchcock, the animal usually survives and shows complete recovery if the exposure to the near vacuum lasts for less than 90 seconds. Exposures of two minutes or longer are almost always fatal. With the exception of the swelling of the body all of the effects are believed to be results of *anoxia,* lack of oxygen. The initial swelling that occurs chiefly in the abdominal region is due to the expansion of gas already present in the body; but the secondary swelling is believed to result from vaporizing of tissue fluids, and is a chief line of evidence supporting the belief that blood and body fluids boil at these low barometric pressures.

In these experiments, the researchers observed that there was marked distension not only in the gas-filled stomach and intestine but also in the bladder. This was no doubt due to the release of dissolved gases from the urine and perhaps also due to the rapid evaporation of this liquid. The edges of the liver were also observed to become rounded, and the liver increased in size and became turgid. The skeletal muscles were observed to swell, and bubbles of gas were seen issuing from the tissue and from the tissue fluids. This swelling gave the appearance of conventional boiling. Considerable amounts of gas that were trapped formed large blisters. The brain herniated through openings in the cranium.

These, then, are some of the known factors that designers must consider before launching an animal-carrying balloon or rocket.

The Aero Medical Laboratory (at the Air Research and Development Command's Wright Air Development Center) has been one of the research groups charged with the problem of rocketing mice and monkeys to great altitudes. The laboratory first decided to tackle such experiments by using a small anesthetized animal, which would as closely as possible resemble man in his reactions. A monkey was placed inside a capsule that was already filled with complex instrumentation for study of the upper atmosphere. The capsule served as the nose of one of the upper atmospheric V–2 rockets.

The results of this initial experiment were disappointing, and several animals died. But collaboration between rocket engineers, electronic and mechanical instrumentation experts and the physiologists continued with a series of participations in five Air Force experiments with V–2s, and with three smaller one-foot-diameter *Aerobee* sounding rockets.

The upper-atmospheric research physicists had already developed techniques for sending complete physics laboratories far into the chemosphere. As we recall, these complex probes made observations while in flight and telemetered back the results. Although it was highly desirable that parachute systems return the flying laboratories undamaged, it was not essential. But to the aeromedical experts, recovery was necessary. They had to know whether the animals being carried experienced any undue strains that would result in harmful aftereffects.

According to a report by Dr. James P. Henry of the Aero Medical Laboratory, the whole instrument rack was shaped to fit within the parachuted nose-capsule of the rocket; pressure, temperature and high accelerations in the long axis of the capsule were measured by appropriate gauges. Three low-range electrical accelerometers measured the subgravity forces that developed in the nose cone during the upward coasting of the rocket after cutoff of the motors, and during the free fall of the nose after its separation from the main body at zenith.

Two monkeys rode in the laboratory. One was seated upright and was connected to an amplifier recording heart action on an electrocardiogram. The other monkey lay across the rocket; he had tiny plastic tubes in an artery and in a vein. The tubes led to electrical transducers which converted the pressure in the blood vessels into signals. The signals were fed through electronic circuitry into a radio transmitter in the nose of the rocket which connected with a special antenna. The transmissions were picked up by the big receiving stations on the rocket range, and there were converted into the recordings familiar to the physician and physiologist.

All kinds of difficulties expected and unexpected in this type work were encountered, but slowly, in successive flights, the partial results were pieced together. They gave a picture that fulfilled theoretical work and confirmed parallel experiments on the human centrifuge and in aircraft. The capsule gave adequate environmental protection, its temperature and pressure not changing significantly, and the breathing pattern and blood pressure of the lightly anesthetized animals were undisturbed. Both acceleration and subgravity states were experienced in the 2,000 mile-per-hour, 38- to 75-mile-altitude flights. The oxygen supply and dehumidifying carbon-dioxide absorber maintained sea-level conditions. The parachute system attached to the capsule imposed no shocks that were not readily absorbed by the rubber bed and nylon crash harness of the animals. The landings from the relatively low *Aerobee* altitudes were so gentle that the apparatus was undamaged, needing only checking to be flown again. The animals did not show any ill effects after the experiments.

With successive experiments the complexity of the instrumentation in the rocket laboratory grew. Finally, a gravity-free experiment was conducted based on the activities of two white mice placed side by side in a drum driven at a rate of four revolutions per minute. This was mounted with its axle across the long axis of the rocket. One mouse had a little shelf to which he could cling, while the other mouse was in a smooth-walled compartment. A camera was installed to record their actions. The film showed that as long as the animal had some object to which he could hold and orient himself, he was essentially undisturbed by the weightless state. The other animal, without an object to cling to, became panicky, but when the parachute opened, arresting free fall and imposing a steady descent, each animal resumed his normal walking and jumping activity, keeping in pace with the drum.

"The entire series of experiments showed that the stresses imposed by a brief rocket flight into the ionosphere, and by the operation of this particular escape-capsule system, are well within the range of tolerance of the animals used, and probably of man as well," says Dr. Henry. "More important still, the work showed that tests of physiological and even psychological reactions can be conducted by proxy and in miniature scale by using animals. The next step awaits the development of rockets of significantly greater performance. Were such vehicles to become available it should be possible to telemeter physiological information in spite of a fourfold or even greater increase in distance from the Earth."

The aeromedical scientists are now waiting for the opportunity to put mice and monkeys aboard actual satellites. And the design considerations for a mouse-carrying satellite have already been established. They will closely resemble the design patterns employed by the rocket people at Wright Air Development Center and the Space Biological Branch of the Aeromedical Field Laboratory at Holloman Air Force Base. Experiments carried out by the latter institution, requiring exposure of animals to primary cosmic radiation at altitudes above 17 miles on 24-hour balloon flights, led to the development of environmental control techniques that definitely must be used in any inhabited satellite experiment. The task of designing and building an animal-carrying satellite requires that we fully understand these techniques.

Simple methods for supplying oxygen and removing carbon dioxide must be developed. Internal capsule temperatures must be maintained at close to normal room temperatures. The balloon flights have proved that the temperature can be controlled by providing adequate insulation, by using animal heat at night, and by cooling the capsule with a water-can cooler during the day. We must keep in mind that an altitude of 17 miles means that space-equivalent conditions are encountered here.

The remarkable results of the balloon flights were revealed in a detailed report at a Rocket Society meeting in 1955 by Major D. C. Simons, chief of the Space Biological Branch, and First Lieutenant O. P. Parks, chief of the Space Biophysics Section at Holloman Air Force Base. The animal capsules, according to this report, were designed to maintain a minimum pressure of 13 to 14 pounds per square inch, and temperatures between 65 and 80 degrees Fahrenheit. Carbon-dioxide absorbing apparatus was used, but no special consideration was given to humidity control. It was not found necessary.

The design of the animal capsule was determined by equipment available, and the requirement for a minimum mass of absorbing material above the specimens to permit maximum exposure to cosmic particles. To obtain the most exposure possible, each flight was usually designed for 24 to 30 hours' duration. Balloon performance being strongly dependent upon pay-load weight, each control technique and every change in design was critically evaluated to obtain maximum reliability with minimum weight. The capsule consisted of two 1/32-inch-thick hemispheres of spun aluminum, which sealed between them a load plate that carried the experimental animals. The 24-inch-diameter pressurized sphere was enclosed in a two-inch-thick cover of Styrofoam or lockfoam to provide thermal insulation. Oxygen cylinders were attached to the load harness which formed a sling that carried the capsule on the balloon load line.

The report emphasized that temperature-control considerations are influenced profoundly by the fact that heat at tropospheric pressures is established largely by air conduction, whereas, in the upper stratosphere, temperature control is determined almost exclusively by radiation. Conductive heat exchange between the capsule and the air above 18 miles has proved negligible. At the Earth's surface, however, air temperature and rate of air flow are significant factors in determining capsule temperature.

Measurements of surface temperatures on a capsule floating above the clouds showed that during the daytime the top and bottom temperatures of the capsule were about 130 degrees and 30 degrees Fahrenheit, respectively. The number and altitude of clouds influenced the bottom temperature considerably. Clouds during the daytime increased the temperature and clouds at night decreased it. Thus, temperature control for a daytime, eight-hour flight posed an entirely different problem than control for a continuous 24-hour flight, where the same system must handle the day and night situations.

At a floating altitude of approximately 25 miles, the capsule-surface radiation temperatures averaged about normal room temperature, this temperature being brought about by a stable internal temperature of 68 degrees Fahrenheit. At night such a capsule would become insufferably cold, and it would become insufferably hot during the day if more than a few heat-producing animals were placed in it.

Experience proved that three inches of Styrofoam or lockfoam insulation was sufficient to keep a capsule full of mice or guinea pigs comfortable at night without any additional heat source. With a method for removing the heat produced by the animals during the daytime, excellent temperature control could be expected throughout a 24-hour flight.

A refrigeration system was devised based on the fact that at the low atmospheric pressure found above 18 miles' altitude, water boils at a temperature at least 10 degrees below normal room temperature. Theoretically, at 21 miles' altitude, water boils at 32 degrees Fahrenheit. The water can, used for cooling purposes, was simply vented to the outside so that it would remain cold at high altitudes. This water can was located in a chamber below the animals. Whenever the animal chamber became too warm, a thermostat activated a blower which circulated the warm air around the cooler-can.

Approximately 85 per cent of the oxygen consumed by mammals is exhaled as carbon dioxide. The maximum tolerable level within the capsule was about 3 per cent carbon dioxide, and therefore a continuously operating reliable system for removal of carbon dioxide was essential. The commonest and most readily available absorbent is soda lime. Granular lithium hydroxide has been used in other applications and would offer a saving in weight, although this chemical is considerably more expensive.

On early flights, carrying relatively few animals, the absorbent material was simply placed in screened containers. As the animal loads increased, it became necessary to use a forced-draft system to ensure efficient utilization of the absorbent. A simple fan blower forced air through a polyethylene tube filled with soda lime. This technique has proved satisfactory and reliable.

The need to control humidity, from a purely medical point of view, depends directly on temperature. At low room temperatures, a high relative humidity causes little discomfort. When ambient temperature approaches body temperature above 95 degrees Fahrenheit, a high relative humidity becomes critical.

Under flight conditions, the capsule humidity dropped during the warm daytime, and increased only at night when the capsule was cool, making increased humidity tolerable. By carefully minimizing the factors that increased humidity, and by taking advantage of factors that decreased it, the scientists found that no special humidity-absorbing device was required.

The sources of water vapor within the capsule comprised expired air and urine, the latter being much the larger source. Therefore, urine was held by an absorbent pad which permitted some humidity control.

Water vapor was precipitated on the water can, capsule walls, and absorbed by the carbon-dioxide absorber. Operation of the water-can cooling system during the daytime maintained the relative humidity between 60 and 80 per cent. This occurred because the warm air from the animal chamber was circulated around the water can which was 20 to 40 degrees cooler. Condensed water was drained to an absorbent pad, which captured it as a liquid to prevent its returning to vapor. At night, heat produced by the animals was lost through the capsule walls. As this situation reached equilibrium, the capsule walls became five to ten degrees cooler than the air in the capsule. Water condensing on these walls held the relative humidity between 90 and 95 per cent. The soda-lime carbon-dioxide absorbing unit was adjusted to a low rate of air flow both to minimize battery drain, and to prevent saturation of the absorbent with water vapor.

We remember that pressurization is one of the most important factors that must be considered. Furthermore, the composition of the capsule atmosphere must be carefully balanced; a correct pressure must remain in the capsule to prevent the animals from experiencing hypoxia. With 21 per cent oxygen, the pressure must be 14.7 pounds per square inch, the same as at sea level; with 100 per cent oxygen, the pressure would be 3.6 pounds per square inch. However, a pure oxygen atmosphere poses a serious fire hazard, and most mammals develop congestion when subjected to more than an 80 per cent oxygen atmosphere at 15 pounds per square inch.

These detailed studies, with emphasis on the capsule mechanics, as well as on the physiological aspects of the experiments, have proved quite valuable. The way in which the experiments were conducted was highly scientific, and Major Simon and Lieutenant Parks's report deserves much attention. It most certainly will be used as a standard for the designers of animal-carrying satellites during the next few years.

In view of these experiments, it is interesting to recall the remarkable proposal revealed by Cornelius Ryan a few years ago in *Collier's* magazine, Dr. Wernher von Braun's *Baby Space Station*. This satellite represents what we might launch as the first inhabited space vehicle within a few years. The Baby Space Station looks like a 30-foot ice-cream cone, topped by a cross of curved mirrors which are to draw power from the Sun. The station's tapered casing contains a complicated maze of measuring instruments, pressure gauges, thermometers, microphones and Geiger counters, all connected to a network of radio, radar and television transmitters which keep the tracking stations on Earth informed about what is going on inside.

At about 18,000 miles per hour the satellite would make one circuit around the Earth every 90 minutes—nearly 16 round trips a day. At dawn and dusk, the vehicle, traveling from horizon to horizon in about seven minutes, would be visible to the naked eye.

Three rhesus monkeys—rhesus, because that species is small and highly intelligent—would live aboard the satellite, feeding from automatic food dispensers. Every move they made would be watched, through television, by observers on Earth.

As fast as the recording instruments gathered information, it would be relayed to the ground; as many as 50 reporting devices could be hooked to a single transmitter that would send out a series of tonal waves. A receiver on Earth would pick up the tangled signals and a decoding machine would unscramble the tones and record the information which would provide a complete story of the happenings on the Baby Space Station.

The monkeys would live in two chambers of a special compartment. In the smaller section, one of the creatures would lie strapped to a seat throughout the test, which might take two months. His hands and head would be free, so he could feed himself, but his body would be bound and covered with a jacket to keep him from freeing himself or from tampering with the measuring instruments taped to his body. The delicate recording devices would provide vital information—body temperature, breathing cycle, pulse rate, heartbeat, blood pressure and so forth.

The other two monkeys, separated from their pinioned companion so that they could not turn him loose, would move about freely in the larger section. During the flight from Earth, these two monkeys, under a mild anesthetic, would be strapped to shock-absorbing rubber couches, to ameliorate the discomfort of the acceleration. By the time the anesthetic wore off, the satellite would have settled in its circular path about the Earth, and a simple timing device would release the two monkeys. They would then float weightlessly inside the cabin.

What would they do? Succumb to fright? Perhaps cower in a corner for two months and slowly starve to death? "I don't think so," says von Braun. "Chances are they would adjust quickly to their new condition. We would make it easier for them to get around by providing leather handholds along the walls, like subway straps, and by stringing a rope across the chamber."

The *Collier's* article goes on to describe the feeding problem. The monkeys would prepare to cope with it on the ground. For month before take-off, the two unbound monkeys would live in a replica of the compartment they would occupy in space, learning to operate food and liquid dispensers. In space, each of the two free animals would have his own feeding station. At specific intervals a klaxon horn would sound, the monkeys responding by rushing to the feeding stations as they had been trained to do. Their movements would break an electric-eye beam, and clear plastic doors would snap shut behind them, sealing them off from their living quarters. Then, an air blower would flush out the living compartment—for sanitary reasons and to keep weightless refuse from blocking the television lenses. The plastic doors would spring open again when the housecleaning was finished.

The monkeys would drink by sucking plastic bottles. Liquid left free, without gravity to keep it in place, would hang in globules. To get solid food, each of the monkeys—again responding to their training—would press a lever on a dispenser much like a candy or cigarette machine. The lever would open a door, enabling the animals to reach in for their food. They would get about half a pound of food a day—a biscuit made of wheat, soybean meal and bone meal, enriched with vitamins. The immobilized monkey would have the same food, his dispensers within easy reach.

Before take-off, the satellite vehicle would resemble one of today's high-altitude rockets, except that it would be a three-stage rocket 150 feet tall, twice the length of a *Vanguard* vehicle. The rocket would take off vertically and then tilt into a shallow path nearly parallel to the Earth. As the third stage of the vehicle reaches an altitude of 60 miles and a speed of 17,700 miles per hour, the final bank of motors would shut off automatically. The conical nose section would coast unpowered to the 200-mile orbit. The entire flight would take 48½ minutes. After the satellite reached its orbit, the automatic pilot would switch the motors on once again to boost the velocity to the speed required to balance the Earth's gravity at that altitude.

Once the satellite entered its orbit, gyroscopically controlled flywheels would turn the nose until it pointed toward the Earth. At the same time, five small antennas would spring out from the cone's sides and a small explosive charge would blast off the nose cap which served to guard the TV lens during the ascent.

Finally, the satellite's power-plant system of mirrors, which were designed to catch the Sun's rays and turn solar heat into electrical energy, would rise into place at the broad end of the cone. A battery-operated electric timer would start a hydraulic pump that would push out a telescopic rod. At the end of the rod would be three curved mirrors. Mercury-filled pipes would run along the mirrors, and plates; the heated mercury would operate generators providing 12 kilowatts of power. Batteries would take over the power functions while the satellite was passing through the shadow of the Earth.

At strategic points over the Earth's surface, 20 or more receiving stations, most of them set up in big trailers, would track the satellite by radar as it passed overhead and would record the television and telemetering broadcasts on tape and film. Because the satellite's radio waves would travel in straight lines, the trailers could pick up broadcasts for just a few minutes at a time—only while the vehicle remained in sight as it traveled from horizon to horizon.

As the weeks passed, the satellite, dragging against the thin air, would drop lower and lower in its orbit. When it descended into fairly dense air, its skin would be heated by friction, causing the temperature to rise within the animal compartments. At last, a thermostat would set off an electric relay which would trigger a capsule containing a quick-acting lethal gas. The monkeys would die instantly and painlessly, according to von Braun. "Soon afterward, the telemetering equipment would go silent, as the rush of air ripped away the solar mirrors which provided power, and the Baby Space Station would begin to glow red. Then suddenly the satellite would disappear in a long white streak of brilliant light—marking the spectacular finish of man's first step in the conquest of space."

Successful research with satellites containing live animals will encourage us considerably in our attempt to tackle manned space flight. The next step in inhabited satellite flight will be found in an idea conceived by the eminent ex-German Peenemünde missile engineer Krafft A. Ehricke, now with the Convair Division of General Dynamics Corporation. His first presentation of a combination aircraft-satellite vehicle was given as the feature lecture at the Congress of the International Astronautical Federation two days after President Eisenhower announced the basketball project.

We know that the establishment of satellites requires a certain minimum altitude, in order to keep them outside the technically significant atmosphere for a certain length of time. The minimum altitude depends on the satellite's shape and the desired orbital lifetime. For a spherically shaped vehicle, for a lifetime of about one year, the required initial altitude of the satellite is approximately 200 miles. Because the drag is still significant at high altitudes, a correspondingly minute thrust force is all that is required to resist the drag force, thereby preventing a decay of the orbit.

At lower altitudes of about 75 miles, the satellite would have a lifetime of only one hour. Thus, if we want to operate a vehicle to circle the Earth at these lower altitudes, Ehricke says we must sustain the vehicle's speed by means of propulsive power which is just strong enough to overcome the drag. The drag at these altitudes is very small and consequently the thrust can be very small. With a normal propellant load of 60 per cent of the initial weight, the vehicle could orbit a number of times around the Earth. In this respect, the vehicle behaves as a satellite. However, the need for power constitutes an important difference from a true satellite. Therefore, Ehricke suggests the designation *satelloid,* a type of vehicle which would operate under small but continuous power. High flight speed in conjunction with low drag makes it possible to maintain the thrust over a significant number of revolutions. The vehicle could follow a circular path around the Earth at circular velocity.

Because of the limitations in rocket propulsion, the satelloid cannot stay in its orbit for periods comparable even to those of short-life satellites. But the satelloid system can operate for a period of five, 10, 20, or even more revolutions at altitudes at which a satellite could not exist for even two or three revolutions. Because the satelloid is under power, the crew (if we assume a manned system) will never be completely weightless. There seems to be a great difference between no weight and even a minute amount of weight. The pilot will always have a control force (jet control) readily available for stability and navigation. Remote-controlled satelloids could also be designed, possibly to carry research animals.

Two operational aspects of satelloids have been studied so far, the high-altitude satelloid, which flies between 150 and 200 miles' altitude, and the low-altitude satelloid, which flies between 80 and 100 miles. Because of the low air density at the higher altitudes, and correspondingly lower resistance to a body passing through it, the high-altitude satelloid needs only a small amount of thrust to keep it in its orbit. The lower-altitude satelloid, which must pass through denser air, requires a relatively high amount of thrust in order to keep flying. From a power standpoint then, which is quite a critical one, high-altitude satelloids are the more feasible.

The propulsion methods and the selection of orbital flight paths for satelloid-type vehicles will not cause undue problems for the rocket experts. Through simple mathematics they can determine the relationship between orbits, gravitational pull and required thrust. The feasibility of satelloid experiments is obvious. But the design and construction of a satelloid is quite another study. Can we build such vehicles in view of today's rocket technology? The step from a 20- or 30-pound basketball satellite to one carrying a passenger load of three monkeys is quite substantial—not to speak of stepping to the point where we shall consider sending a craft aloft with humans aboard.

11. From Satellites to Satelloids

When the father of space rocketry, Professor Hermann Oberth, read Eisenhower's satellite announcement, he said: "The basketball-sized globe filled with recording and transmitting devices is of course the first step. There must be not only one but many of these, each a little larger and more revealing than its predecessor. Small animals will go up in them first, then large animals and finally a man—the pioneer in space. How I wish I could be that man! Columbus, Magellan, Balboa, all the great adventurers of the past will be shadows behind him in the history books of tomorrow . . ."

There is an expression that gives the attitude of the scientific mind. "Nothing that is theoretically possible will remain untried." During their time on Earth, humans have been confined animals. But now that man has reached the point when the first unmanned satellites will circle the globe, he certainly will look toward the other planets with great anticipation. Professor Oberth's dreams are about to come true.

We know that larger satellites circling the globe at distances of 800 or more miles from the Earth might remain in their orbits indefinitely. However, when a satellite's gyros begin to deviate from their original settings—resulting in the batteries going dead, because the solar pickups will be turning away from the Sun—the scientific value of the satellite will be drastically reduced. It is vital to those sciences that depend upon the satellite's being in a permanent orbit that the path be maintained. Even if the orbiter could be brought back to Earth, perhaps by help of reversed rocket thrust and parachute descent, so that the gyros might be reset and other adjustments made, it would be almost impossible to get the satellite back to its original orbit.

It would be possible, however, to "fly" up to the satellite with a manned satelloid-type vehicle, make physical contact and adjust the gyros and other mechanisms with the help of automatic devices. By building a manned vehicle we would also be gathering the experience needed for the design of tomorrow's superairplanes, military and civilian, and for attempting further conquests of space. It cannot be stressed too much how valuable it would be to have a manned satelloid vehicle circle the Earth, even if it would do so for only a very short time.

Two satelloid projects are currently undergoing development. North American Aviation, builders of the *Sabrejet,* in co-operation with the National Advisory Committee for Aeronautics (NACA), the Navy and the Air Force, is constructing a satelloid sometimes referred to as the X–15. Douglas Aircraft Company, builders of the *Skyrocket,* is speeding work on the second satelloid under a contract with ONR.

While a service ceiling of 100 miles has been mentioned for the North American craft, ONR says that the Douglas ship will soar to 140 miles. As we know, the air that these planes will traverse at the top of their flight will be as thin as a laboratory vacuum-chamber.

ONR believes that the Douglas satelloid can use existing rocket motors and still stay below an acceleration that would destroy the pilot. The best take-off procedure is one in which the craft is launched into the air from the belly of a high-flying bomber. According to ONR's plans, the pilot will have complete control of his craft, steering it with control surfaces while it is still in the atmosphere. When the air thins out too much, he will control his vehicle by firing small rockets set at an angle to the fuselage.

Speeds in the neighborhood of 4,000 to 5,000 miles per hour have been mentioned for the North American craft. The Douglas craft's top speed will be about 3,500 miles per hour, with the flight taking at most 20 minutes and covering a horizontal distance of about 500 miles. Although the first manned space vehicles will be satelloid-type rocket aircraft—highly advanced in design and construction—they are not true satelloids, because they are not designed to travel farther than 500 miles. A true satelloid must be capable of circling the globe at least once. The phrase spaceship is not precisely descriptive either, because the satelloid-type rocket aircraft will do the greatest portion of its travel through the atmosphere, visiting in space for perhaps only a few minutes. Nevertheless, the building of these vehicles will initiate the satelloid phase of aeronautics.

Some pilots have already mastered the technique of vertical take-off (VTO). The flights have proved that such take-offs are safe and practical for many purposes. The crew of tomorrow's true satelloid craft will need such experience, as they must be able to gauge the effects of high vertical accelerations. If, for example, the craft represents the second or third stage of a huge step-rocket, accelerations in the neighborhood of eight to 10 times that of gravity might be experienced for a brief period. By the time such a manned craft leaves its boosters, the velocity might be in the neighborhood of 10,000 to 12,000 miles per hour, and the altitude could be anywhere between 100 and 200 miles.

The satelloid would have to gain another 6,000 miles per hour if it were to travel at the same velocity as unmanned satellites, or if it were to make physical contact with one of the satellites and remain in its orbit for any length of time. At this point, the achievement of a 6,000 mile-per-hour velocity gain is really not considered the greatest problem. The air resistance at high altitude is close to zero. Speeds up to 6,000 miles per hour probably could be achieved by rocket aircraft already in existence, if these craft were launched at a sufficient distance from the earth.

While our engineers will not have too much difficulty launching these craft—using the step-rocket principle or the mother-airplane method—and while the vehicles can be equipped with adequate engines, the designers will have the difficult task of protecting the pilot or crew from the hazards of space. Another task ahead is the practical design of the satelloid itself.

Two important factors contributing to our successful construction of satelloid rocket craft are the early German work on rocket air-planes, and the painstaking research of our National Advisory Committee for Aeronautics. In planning intensive exploration of the high-speed range—the first approach to space flight—the Air Force, Navy, aircraft manufacturers and NACA joined forces after World War II. Because the necessary research information could not be obtained in the laboratory—transonic wind tunnels had not been developed then—it was decided that full-size, specially designed, piloted airplanes would be used. These were to be equipped with instruments designed to yield needed data.

The program called for the construction of a series of high-speed airplanes to penetrate the transonic and supersonic speed ranges, and the planes were constructed by four different manufacturers under Air Force or Navy contracts. The designers leaned heavily upon data obtained in NACA wind tunnels and, later, upon pilotless aircraft research at Wallops Island. First to be completed and flown was the famous Bell X-1, which pierced the sonic barrier by October, 1947.

Meanwhile, NACA established the High-Speed Flight Research Station at Muroc, California, which is now called Edwards. At this vast desert air base, home of the Air Force Flight Test Center, research aircraft projects are conducted as a co-operative venture by NACA, the military services and the aircraft industry. At least eight different research airplanes have been built here, plus a number of duplicates.

All these custom-built, highly instrumented research vehicles were designed for the investigation of airplane configurations that promised certain advantages for high-speed and high-altitude flight. Some were intended for transonic studies, some for supersonic, some for obtaining data about space flight. A variety of wing shapes explored the possibilities of straight, swept, movable and triangular wings. The power plants were of turbojet, turbojet with afterburner, or rocket type.

One aim of the program was the investigation of stability and control by means of recording instruments and pilot's opinion. This was a major study with each of the research airplanes.

Air loads imposed on the wings, tail, and fuselage during maneuvers were other studies of prime importance. These loads were measured by scores of *strain gauges* and *air-pressure pickups* placed at strategic points, principally on the wings and tail. The strain gauges measured the aerodynamic strains, while the pressure pickups plotted a detailed pattern of pressure distribution.

In a typical test, a research airplane may be provided with 100 to 200 strain gauges and about 400 pressure orifices. During maneuvers, measurements are recorded by automatic equipment. Even though compact lightweight instruments are used, the instrumentation and wiring installed in a research airplane often weigh 500 pounds or more.

The findings indicate that a rocket craft employed in a visit to the orbits where man-made moons will be circling might look very much like the current supersonic aircraft, such as the X–3 or F–104. The cockpit will probably be large enough to hold a two-man crew and the aircraft will be streamlined and have wings and control surfaces for return to Earth.

Although some designers and engineers have some experience in constructing and operating high-altitude rocket planes, not too many rocket aircraft have flown. The Germans worked on a number of rocket-propelled fighters of which the Me 163B was the first to see operational service in 1944. The Me 163B had sharply swept wooden wings and a high fin but no horizontal tail. The rocket unit burned a mixture of concentrated hydrogen peroxide and hydrazine hydrate mixed with alcohol, which were carried in separate tanks and pumped by a turbine to the combustion chamber. The rocket developed a maximum thrust of 3,300 pounds at a fuel consumption of 1,000 pounds per minute, which gave a climb to 40,000 feet within four minutes, and a range after reaching that height of 22 miles, which would be extended by gliding. Poor aerodynamic qualities restricted the top velocity to 550 miles per hour at 40,000 feet.

During the last decade, rocket aircraft have been built in the Soviet Union, France, Great Britain and the United States. The first American rocket engine designed for aircraft propulsion was developed by Reaction Motors, Inc. This was the unit used in the world's first supersonic aircraft, the Bell X–1. The motor consists of four cylindrical combustion chambers, each with a separate igniter so that they can be used individually or together. The motor components and fuel system are supported within a frame of steel, the whole unit weighing only 210 pounds. The fuel, a mixture of ethyl alcohol and water, is circulated around the combustion chambers. Both the fuel and liquid oxygen are injected separately under pressure into the front of the combustion chamber, where the chemical reaction produces a jet velocity of many thousand feet per second. The thrust obtained was 1,500 pounds for each chamber, or a total maximum thrust of 6,000 pounds.

The Douglas *Skyrocket* which passed the speed of sound in

straight and level flight at 26,000 feet in July, 1949, and attained 1,324 miles per hour at 72,000 feet in June, 1951, was originally designed to use a rocket and a turbojet simultaneously. Built to fly at 1,820 miles per hour at 75,000 feet, the airplane was first equipped with a turbojet engine supplied with 250 gallons of ordinary aviation fuel giving a 30-minute endurance, and the Reaction Motors rocket unit. This was the rocket used in the Bell X–1, and the total rocket endurance by using the chambers individually was about three and one half minutes. At maximum power the endurance was less than one minute. To save fuel, assistance-take-off (ATO) rocket units were also used. Later, the turbojet engine was abandoned and the space saved was used to increase the supply of propellant for a new rocket engine, which incorporated several small modifications of the unit used in the Bell X–1.

A B–29 *Superfortress* was employed as a mother aircraft to carry the *Skyrocket*, fitted to the bomb bays, to 35,000 feet. Here, the rocket craft was launched. A considerable quantity of fuel was lost by evaporation before the *Skyrocket* was launched. By the time the pilot, William Bridgeman, had reached altitude with the *Skyrocket*, only 15 per cent of his fuel supply was left. This gave him an endurance of about three minutes' powered flight for his record-breaking run, during which he maintained a velocity of over 1,000 miles per hour for about 10 seconds. For the new Douglas satelloid-type craft, the mother aircraft will no doubt carry rocket fuel so that it can fill up the tank.

Latest and most advanced of all rocket aircraft is the Bell X–2. With this airplane we are really on our way toward cosmic flight, and the experience that we shall gather with this plane will help us in our efforts to produce manned satellite vehicles.

Designed specifically to investigate heat and speed problems encountered well beyond the speed of sound, the X–2 is used solely as a flying research laboratory. From a drag and power standpoint, the X–2 is designed to surpass the speed of the Bell X–1A which reached 1,653 miles an hour in December, 1953. A number of glide tests with the sharply swept-back X–2 have proved the soundness of its novel design. The X–2 incorporates many innovations, among them being the use of stainless steel and *K-monel*, a super alloy, in the fuselage and wings. These metals have a much higher melting point than aluminum. A unique landing gear, incorporating a flat lightweight skid rather than wheels, has added considerably to the time the X–2 can stay in the air. Additional fuel can be carried in the space ordinarily occupied by wheels and retracting gear. The X–2 is powered by a rocket engine capable of developing power almost equal to that developed by a modern naval cruiser, illustrating the tremendous power necessary to drive the X–2.

Special provisions have been made in the X–2 for the pilot's safety. The cabin is heavily insulated, pressurized and detachable. Explosive charges are used to separate the entire cabin from the rest of the airplane in case the pilot has to leave the X–2 at high altitudes. A ribbon-type parachute will carry the capsule to a low altitude where the pilot can bail out.

As with the Bell X–1, a bomber has been adapted to carry the new plane to the altitude where the craft begins its flight. This allows the experimental airplane to start operations with a much greater fuel load, thereby permitting flights of longer duration.

The first manned vehicles to explore space must be conservative in concept and design. The early trips, dozens and dozens of them, will be scouting ones in order for the crew to gather experience and to test the performance and design of the craft. And when the first manned satelloid operation is attempted, the ship will not carry any pay load. Later the purpose of a trip might be to adjust the gyros of an already existing satellite. This will be done with the help of automatic devices so designed that the crew does not have to leave the rocket craft while working on the satellite.

Norman L. Baker, of Indiana Technical College, has suggested that a manned space-craft vehicle might be powered by a combination of rocket and air-breathing power plants. The plane would have a delta configuration with large surface areas and flat underside for dissipating skin friction heating and for gliding in the rarefied regions of the extreme upper atmosphere. Presently available power plants and propellants could be used for this craft. Two turbojet engines would carry the craft aloft to an altitude from 10 to 12 miles, using fuel contained in droppable external cells for this portion of the flight. The loss in value of the mass ratio, due to the weight of the air-breathing power plants, is considered to be logistically offset by the elimination of a mother ship, and by providing a means for positive controlled return flight to base. At high altitudes, away from high aerodynamic drag, the program would consist of steadily increasing speed to obtain progressively larger parabolic-arc flight paths. With maximum load, the take-off from the Earth's surface would be aided by liquid- or solid-propellant assisted-take-off units. When such a program has progressed beyond the experimental stage, the vehicle could be modified to meet the performance expectations of the satelloid vehicles.

Why not go a step further and develop a configuration that has droppable outer-wing sections and engines as well as droppable fuel tanks? The flight pattern for this craft might follow this scheme: the ship will take off under its own power, using four powerful turbojets, will climb to 12 miles, and then be refueled by a tanker aircraft. Still climbing gently, the satellite-type craft will approach supersonic velocity at 14 miles. At this point, the four turbojets, the wing tanks and the outer-wing sections will be released and dropped. Using the remaining kerosene-type fuel, two ram-jet engines will carry the now smaller and lighter aircraft to 25 or 30 miles' altitude. At this height, the ram-jets will be jettisoned and the craft—again lighter—will streak upward under the impetus of its rocket engines. In this case, no rocket fuel has been used to reach the starting point, which is already about 30 miles high. From this level, no excess weight is carried.

For guiding a satelloid-type craft into a specific orbit, intricate radar and ground-guidance facilities might be required. It is probable that throttling the craft's rocket engines and operation of rocket thrust steering will eventually be handled automatically in accordance with a previously plotted flight plan. The acceleration and rapid velocity gain of the craft will probably not permit the crew to attempt any manned control, and not until the high-flying craft is in its orbit will the crew actually begin to pilot their plane.

The radio signals sent to the ship from the ground will release bursts of rocket thrust from time to time as the vehicle follows the elliptical path leading into the orbit. Finally, when the ship has reached the orbit, the pilot will be instructed to take over. If he is to fly his ship as a satelloid, he must apply power continuously. But if the orbit is more than 200 miles from the Earth, the vehicle will have become another satellite and there is no need for the pilot to use any power to keep the ship moving.

The craft may arrive at the apogee, or high point, of the orbit with the vehicle's longitudinal axis at right angles to the flight path, or even tail first. Only special instruments can tell a pilot where he is with respect to the desired orbit.

The pilot of an airplane adjusts the position of his craft by using the horizon as a scale of reference. But in space he has no horizon. Once a rocket ship reaches an orbit, in order to stay there, the pilot must first rotate the ship into exactly the right direction, so he must have a horizon, even if it is an artificial one.

The use of spinning flywheels within the rocket ship has been suggested by Professor Oberth and Wernher von Braun. We know that a force equal to that of the spinning force will be exerted on the rocket ship itself, but in the opposite direction. As the flywheel is much lighter than the rocket ship, the wheel must make many revolutions before the rocket craft makes one. Nevertheless, by placing an electric motor within even a relatively small flywheel, we can rotate nearly any vehicle in empty space. But one flywheel alone will not be enough, since a freely suspended body in space has three degrees of freedom—the ship can nose up and down, turn left and right, and also roll around its longitudinal axis. Therefore, three electrically powered flywheels, spinning at right angles to each other, are necessary. Once we have established a horizon, or scale of reference, we can determine the required angular corrections of the ship in the three degrees of freedom, and let the three wheels run until the ship has attained the desired position.

Wernher von Braun employs this system in his larger space-vehicle designs, and undoubtedly this method will apply to any space craft, even to unmanned satellites. To perform this stabilization, an intricate mechanism is used. Called an *automatic-positioning device*, this instrumentation comprises a small platform suspended in a gimbal system. The platform's position is stabilized by three gyroscopes, each stabilizing one degree of freedom. Also, on the platform at either end are two small swivel-mounted telescopes, each equipped with a system of photoelectric cells. The pilot, or the navigator, sights each telescope on a star and locks each instrument on its star by energizing the photoelectric cells. In this way, he establishes a reference plane defined by the two stars and the rocket ship itself. This is the "horizon." On this horizon, a three-dimensional co-ordinate system can be erected with the rocket ship as the center. By consulting his navigational charts, the pilot can develop the necessary bearings of his ship. The figures thus obtained will be applied to the scales on each of the suspension axes of the gimbal system, and the little servomotors that rotate these will be started. The stabilizing process then begins as the whole gimbal system slowly swings around into the correct heading. Once it has settled in the correct position, the three flywheels are set in motion and automatically continue to run until the rocket ship is positioned correctly with respect to the controlling stabilized platform. Once the rocket craft is facing in the right direction, the rocket motors are turned on for a few seconds and the velocity increased sufficiently for the craft to remain in its orbit.

To make physical contact with an unmanned satellite, assuming that the manned craft could be directed into the unmanned satellite's orbit, would be a delicate maneuver, and a large portion of fuel would have to be saved for such a rendezvous. The pilot would most likely use electronic instruments coupled to the rocket engines and the automatic-positioning system, so designed that they would guide and propel the craft toward the satellite. Only insignificant amounts of rocket thrust, or even small bursts of compressed gas, would be needed to increase the velocity required to catch up with the satellite. Physical contact may be made by a system somewhat similar to the boom refueling methods used by our bombers. With too great a velocity, the space craft would push the satellite ahead and increase its orbital velocity, which event, of course, must be avoided. Successful accomplishment of these difficult operations might require a two-man crew.

Other than the problems connected with steering or guiding and stabilizing the craft, mechanical problems met include air conditioning and cooling the rocket vehicle. For cooling supersonic aircraft designed for flight up to 10 miles, conventional simple-type air-cycle systems become inadequate.

In view of the generation of an envelope of hot air around the fast-flying rocket craft, owing to aerodynamic heating as the craft zooms through the lower layers of the atmosphere, we are particularly interested in learning at what altitude aerodynamic or frictional heating can be expected to cease. This question has been partly answered by Dr. Eugen Sänger, who has found that at a height of 80 miles a craft would lose over six miles of altitude per revolution about the Earth as a consequence of air drag. The altitude loss per revolution would be only three feet if the vehicle would circle at a height of 112 miles. Somewhere in the range between 80 and 112 miles' altitude, air drag and simultaneously skin heating for aircraft velocities of about 18,000 miles per hour are considerably reduced.

The temperature problems of rocket flight persist even at greater altitude. Beyond the border of thermal interaction between atmosphere and craft, the skin temperature is determined by the effects of radiations from the Sun. Gleaming white materials such as magnesium oxide can serve as surface coatings if a manned craft is not to become overheated when exposed to the field of these radiations.

In contrast to the present rocket craft, and to the advanced satelloid versions now on the drawing boards, it is interesting to contemplate a more extreme design. This, incidentally, will give us an idea of how big the task of design and construction is. It will also give us some insight into the cost and time required for developing a vehicle for manned flight to outer space.

Dr. Wernher von Braun has also designed such a vehicle and has published the technical calculations, flight characteristics and performance data. His three-stage ship stands 265 feet tall, approximately the height of a 24-story building. The third stage represents the space craft itself. The base of the first stage is 65 feet in diameter. The over-all weight of the configuration is 7,000 tons, about the weight of 100 four-engined airliners.

The three power plants are driven by the combination of nitric acid and hydrazine, which is fed into the rocket motors by turbopumps. Fifty-one rocket motors pushing with a combined thrust of 14,000 tons power the first stage. These motors consume 5,250 tons of propellants within 84 seconds. Thus, in less than a minute and a half, the rocket loses 75 per cent of its original weight.

The second stage, mounted on top of the first, has 34 rocket motors with a total thrust of 1,750 tons and burns 770 tons of propellants. It operates for only 124 seconds.

The third and final stage—carrying crew, equipment and pay load —has five rocket motors with a combined thrust of 220 tons. This body, or cabin stage, of the rocket ship carries 90 tons of propellants, including ample reserves for the return trip to Earth. In addition, it is capable of carrying a cargo or pay load of about 36 tons into an orbit 1,075 miles above sea level. In expectation of the return trip, the nose section has conventional aircraft wings for descent into the Earth's atmosphere. In its design, von Braun's huge vehicle is similar to the two-man satelloid we have already discussed, the difference being in size and performance.

The choice of the take-off site for von Braun's vehicle poses a number of problems. Because of the vast amount of auxiliary equipment—fuel storage tanks and machine shops, radio and radar equipment, astronomical and meteorological stations—an extensive area is required. Furthermore, it is essential that the rocket ship fly over the ocean during the early part of the flight in order that the booster stages may fall to Earth without causing damage. The tiny United States possession known as Johnston Island, in the Pacific, or Patrick Air Force Base have been suggested as bases.

At the launching area, the heavy rocket ship is assembled on a great platform that will be wheeled into place over a tunnellike jet deflector, which drains off the fiery gases of the first stage's rocket motors. Finally, with a mighty roar which can be heard many miles away, the rocket ship slowly takes off—so slowly, that in the first second it travels less than 15 feet. Soon it begins to pick up speed, and 20 seconds later has disappeared into the clouds.

Because of the acceleration, the crew, located in the nose, will be lying flat in contour chairs at take-off, facing upward. Throughout its flight to the orbit, the rocket ship is under the control of an automatic pilot. The timing of the flight and of the various maneuvers must be so precise that only a machine can be trusted to do the job.

After a short interval, the automatic pilot tilts the rocket into a shallow path. By 84 seconds after take-off, when the fuels of the first stage are nearly exhausted, the rocket ship is climbing at a gentle angle of 20 degrees.

When it reaches an altitude of 25 miles, it will have a velocity of about 5,000 miles per hour. To enable the upper stages to break away from the tail section, or first stage, the thrust of the first stage has to be throttled down to almost zero. The motors of the second stage now begin to operate, and the connection between the now useless first stage and the rest of the rocket ship is severed. The tail section drops behind, while the two upper stages of the ship forge ahead.

The same procedure is repeated 124 seconds later. The second stage is dropped into the ocean. The rocket ship by this time has attained an altitude of 40 miles and is more than 300 miles from the take-off site. The vehicle has now reached a velocity of 10,000 miles per hour.

The third and last stage—the nose section, or cabin-equipped spaceship—proceeds under the power of its own rocket motors. Just 84 seconds after the dropping of the second stage, the rocket ship, now moving at 18,000 miles per hour, reaches a height of 63 miles above the Earth.

The moment the rocket reaches its 18,000 miles-per-hour speed the motors are cut off, even though the fuel supply is not exhausted. The ship continues on an unpowered trajectory until it reaches an altitude of 1,075 miles. This is the apogee, in this case exactly half-way around the globe from the take-off point.

In coasting up from 63 miles to 1,075 miles, the rocket ship had been slowed by the Earth's gravitational pull to 15,000 miles per hour. This velocity is not sufficient to keep the ship in the chosen orbit. If the velocity is not increased by the rocket motors to about 17,000 miles an hour, the craft will swing back halfway around the Earth to the 63 miles' altitude. Then the vehicle will continue around until it passes below its first apogee. By this time, the heat of air friction would probably have killed the vehicle's occupants.

An extraordinary fact about the flight of von Braun's rocket craft is that it would take only 56 minutes to reach the desired orbit, during which time the rocket ship would have been powered for only five minutes.

To the rocket ship's crew orbiting in their craft at 1,075 miles' altitude, the Earth would appear to be making one revolution every two hours, instead of every 24 hours. This apparent fast spin of the globe is the only indication the crew has of the tremendous velocity at which their rocket ship is moving.

By all means, we are apt to see such rocket ships within the next two decades, but the first manned vehicles to explore space will be almost insignificant compared with von Braun's ship.

The problems involved in the operation of manned rocket craft at very high altitudes and eventually in free space are of diverse and complex nature. Their solutions require contributions from meteorology, geophysics, astronomy and astrophysics, cosmic-ray physics, aerodynamics, radiobiology, physiology, aviation medicine, space medicine, and human engineering. As pointed out by the space flight expert, Dr. Heinz Haber, physicist at the University of California, difficulties in semantics are frequently encountered owing to the overlapping of the different fields. Particularly, the term *upper atmosphere* is inadequate and misleading, since it conveys different meanings in various fields such as meteorology, geophysics and aviation medicine. For the common benefit, it appears expedient to coin a new term for designating those regions of the atmosphere where, in terms of manned rocket flight, the conditions of conventional aviation blend into those of actual space flight. To this end, the term *aeropause* has been proposed. The aeropause is defined as that region of the atmosphere where normal functioning of man and craft begin to cease and space-equivalent conditions are gradually approached. The concept of the aeropause appears to be quite useful in modern aviation and rocketry. It circumscribes the area characterized by certain factors of environment that are distinctly different from those found in the area of conventional aviation or of space. The aeropause encompasses the region between the 10- and 120-mile levels. Above the aeropause we have "actual space" and actual-space conditions. These involve hazards that must be met and conquered by the crews of satelloids and manned satellites.

12. Survival in Space

For many years now, so far as high-speed flight is concerned, man in the natural state has been left behind and is almost obsolete. And when we consider space flight he is even worse off, because the environment outside the atmosphere, where man was never designed to operate, holds hazards whose extent we cannot even estimate.

Active life of the kind that we know is not conceivable in space. We are dependent upon a relatively high air pressure and a relatively substantial volume of oxygen. Neither is found in space. We are unaccustomed to the different types of original radiations typical of space, such as primary cosmic rays, and unaccustomed to meteoric bombardment, lack of gravity and strange temperature phenomena. While the atmosphere provides us with ample life-sustaining pressure conditions on the one hand, it protects us from the ingredients of space on the other. Where atmospheric conditions cease, we leave behind vitally important factors indigenous to the Earth's atmosphere, and foreign to extraterrestrial space.

In an attempt to analyze and understand these conditions, aeromedical science is now expanding its research field to include what has been termed *space medicine*.

To many people, space medicine appears as a capricious or unrealistic idea in aviation medicine. But it proves to be a logical and necessary step in development, for successful achievement of manned space flight is dependent upon a complete understanding of the physiological and biological aspects of how the human will behave in space.

In anticipation of such developments, a special department, the Department of Space Medicine, was founded in 1949 by the com-

mandant of the USAF School of Aviation Medicine at Randolph
Field, Texas. Problems concerning rocket flights were also being
studied by the Aeromedical Laboratory at Wright Field at about the
same time.

In 1950 the Aero Medical Association proposed the establishment
of a Space Medicine Branch of this organization, and in 1951 this
branch was finally formed with Colonel Paul A. Campbell as its chairman. Dr. H. Strughold, ex-German aeromedical expert, now head of
the USAF Department of Space Medicine, says that the foundation
of this branch was considered necessary in order to have a medical
counterpart of the various societies dealing with rocketry, space
flight, and astronautics.

Today the Space Medical Branch of the Aero Medical Association
offers a special program. "Space medicine is no longer the diffuse
area which it may have appeared to be a few years ago," Strughold
says. The scope of its problems is now clearly defined. They have been
clarified by the introduction of a new concept of the boundaries
between the atmosphere and space based on the function which the
atmosphere has for man and craft.

As we know, at relatively low altitudes the various functions of
the atmosphere cease, one after the other. These levels are the space-
equivalent altitudes. We meet space-equivalent conditions with respect to lack of oxygen at 10 miles, body fluid boiling at 13 miles,
heavy primaries of cosmic radiation at 24 miles, ultraviolet solar
radiation at 27 miles, and meteor collision hazards at 100 miles. Valuable information regarding these conditions has already been obtained from experiments with balloon- and rocket-launched mice
and monkeys.

The Earth, with its magnetic field, its reflection of radiations, and
its mass, modifies some of these conditions, making them different
from those found at high altitudes. Since the bulk of the Earth
gives protection from one half of the cosmic radiation and meteors,
the aeromedical scientists speak of semi-equivalent conditions of
space.

The designers of a manned satellite have a big job to tackle. First,
there is the question of constructing a completely sealed cabin with
air-conditioning and pressurization systems. If an aircraft cabin loses
its pressure at 10 miles, the crew will retain *useful consciousness* for

about 30 seconds. During this brief period they must nose the plane downward into regions having richer air, before the blackout that is sweeping over them turns into death. At 11 miles, the period of useful consciousness diminishes to 15 seconds. At 13 miles, death comes quickly—the atmospheric pressure is so low that water would boil at the corresponding temperature of the human blood.

So far, science has not come up with a satisfactory answer to the problem, although two approaches have been tried. The Navy has developed a heavy rubber suit with accordion-jointed limbs and a helmet that laps down over the crew member's chest. This *full pressure suit* has been described as a true space suit that might be worn even on the Moon. But this suit seems to be a rather incomplete solution. The suit's airtight construction makes it quite uncomfortable to wear, and when the suit is inflated, it blows up like a balloon and the wearer finds walking and even working difficult. It is possible that the full pressure suit can be improved, at least for high-flying aircraft.

The Air Force has developed a suit that can be made so tight that it keeps the water in the wearer's tissues from turning to vapor when the outside pressure fails. This outfit is called a *partial pressure suit*. It is a tight-fitting garment with a rigid helmet that fits over the pilot's head. Inside the suit and along the limbs are flat rubber bladders with flexible tubes connecting to a high-pressure oxygen cylinder. When the cockpit loses its pressure, an automatic valve snaps open, allowing oxygen to flow into the helmet and rubber bladders. Their expansions tighten the suit, supplying a pressure around the pilot's body so that his blood will be kept from boiling. With this suit, the pilot supposedly will be able to stay alive in a vacuum for about ten minutes, and it is believed that he will be able to move with enough freedom to work his controls and perhaps bring his craft down to the denser atmosphere. However, his hands, which are not fully pressurized, would swell up quickly with blood. He would breathe with difficulty. His neck just below his helmet will become a ring of pain. So far, the suit's designers have not been able to make a garment that pressurizes the pilot's neck without causing strangulation. On the other side of the ledger, Lieutenant Colonel Frank Everest, crack Air Force test pilot, owes his life to the suit. The canopy split while he was testing a rocket-powered research craft. He quickly inflated his suit, and brought his plane down without further incident.

A pilot dressed in this way may be able to save his life if his satelloid cockpit is punctured. But he is at such a great altitude that his return to the lower atmosphere cannot possibly be done without risking disintegration of his craft from skin heating.

The space medicine experts are trying their best to work out a solution. Many of them believe that the crew of a spaceship must occupy individual solid-walled cylinders or capsules, each provided with elaborate air-conditioning apparatus. For a two-man satelloid, it is therefore probable that the entire cabin will be built as a separately sealed and self-sustained unit so far as air conditioning and pressurization are concerned, in much the same design as the cockpit of the Bell X–2.

We believe that the so-called space suits will be useless inside a rocket ship; the crew will be too clumsy in their cramped quarters under conditions calling for emergency movements. Of course, the crew may be wearing *g-suits* (fighter-pilot-type suits) for protection against rapid accelerations, and will have emergency oxygen equipment. These g-suits are fairly comfortable and will permit the men to work their controls and instruments at all times.

The crew must be artificially kept under climatic conditions approaching those at sea level. Above 16 miles, this environment cannot be achieved in a conventional pressurized cabin that is fed by air pumped in from the outside atmosphere. The air density at 16 miles is about 4 per cent of the sea-level air density. Because of this fact, the task of using outside air at high altitudes to climatize the cabin is beyond the capabilities of present-day compressors. The mechanical operation of compressing this thin air to physiological levels would also result in the production of intolerable heat. Furthermore, the process is prohibitive from a toxicological point of view. In the upper part of the stratosphere many chemical reactions take place, and of these, the formation of ozone is the most important. Ozone is toxic, irritating the respiratory membranes. For all these reasons, a hermetically sealed cabin in which life-sustaining components of the air are carried in tanks must provide the environment. The altitude at which a hermetically sealed cabin becomes necessary, from a physiological point of view as well as from a technical one, is around 20 miles. When this altitude is reached, the vehicle has no further life-sustaining contact with the Earth. The vehicle becomes a world all its own. At this point we should not forget that satelloids will operate at altitudes up to 200 miles.

Air-conditioning experts seem to think that it will be as complicated to provide breathable air for the interiors of satelloid-type craft as it will be to build the ships themselves. The air-conditioning system in a spaceship would have to control not only interior air temperatures and circulation but also air pressure plus those chemicals and gases that form in the interior.

The absence of gravity means that there would be no natural convection of air in the cabin, and warm air would not rise and be replaced by cold air, as would happen under normal conditions. Therefore, a man confined to a small area such as the interior of a sealed cockpit would quickly be surrounded by the deadly carbon dioxide of his own exhaling, and this would eventually cause suffocation. Machinery and equipment would be affected in the same way and would heat up and be destroyed. Thus, forced circulation of air is essential.

Professor Hermann Oberth suggests that radiant heat from the Sun will be exploited by the spaceship's air-conditioning system of the future. By using the theory that black absorbs heat from the Sun and white reflects it, the radiant heat could be controlled by painting one side of the ship white and the opposite side black. Then one side or the other could be turned toward the Sun, depending on existing needs at the time.

F. H. Green, of AiResearch Manufacturing Company, says that the air in the cabin of a spaceship would have to be used and re-used during a lengthy voyage. This would obviously lead to an accumulation of carbon dioxide and other impurities and poisons in the cabin air if no means were provided to remove them. Carbon dioxide would probably be removed chemically, as in the case of balloon-launched animals, and in much the same way that it is done for submerged submarines. The other impurities would be removed by condensation, wherein the radiation principle would be put to a particularly good use. Air circulating through the air-conditioning system would pass over a surface 100 to 200 degrees Fahrenheit below zero so that impurities would be reduced to liquids and removed.

Humans and many machines are inefficient when humidity reaches far above or below normal, and therefore water would be needed to control humidity in long-range spaceships. In order to save weight, scientists are taking steps to reclaim water from such sources as body waste products and fog in the air-conditioning system. Experiments with balloon-launched monkeys have indicated that it will not be necessary to control humidity in satelloid-type vehicles that will operate for only a few hours.

The problem connected with cosmic radiation is considered even with respect to the operation of small unmanned satellites, and it is of greater importance to know the impact of cosmic radiation on humans. Much apprehension connected with the exposure of crews in high-flying aircraft to primary cosmic radiations in the stratosphere has been eliminated by the Air Research and Development Command. Some of the command's research projects conducted in the Space Biology Branch of the Aero Medical Field Laboratory at Holloman Air Development Center, New Mexico, have yielded valuable data. In particular, the serious questions concerning the effects of cosmic rays upon the human body have been studied intensively. Authorities have often pointed out that the penetration of the cosmic particles into the body of a traveler in the stratosphere or space might cause formation of cataracts of the eye lens, damage to the skin, or permanent destruction of nerve cells, and genetic damage.

We recall that huge plastic balloons proved practical for such experiments since they could remain at altitudes higher than 17 miles for at least 24 hours, long enough to expose experimental subjects (for example, human skulls and tissue) to primary cosmic radiations in the stratosphere. The balloon flights in this instance gave some facts that have dispelled some of the fears we have of cosmic radiation. Some of the animals sent aloft were exposed to cosmic particles above 17 miles for as long as 35 hours.

Of particular importance in these experiments was the effect of cosmic particles upon the central nervous system. If the particles did damage or destroy nerve cells, the performance of the exposed individual would be hindered.

The monkeys sent aloft and exposed to cosmic radiation were observed closely before and after the balloon flights; the animals performed normally after their two flights. After watching the exposed creatures for six months following the experiments, scientists tentatively concluded that cosmic particles may have been overestimated as hazards to the nerve system and that a traveler in the stratosphere should be able to perform duties in a normal manner with no serious aftereffects.

Albino mice were used to establish whether cosmic radiations might cause cataracts to develop on the supersensitive eyes of these animals. However, after being exposed to radiations, the eyes of the mice showed no signs of cataracts.

Other flights indicated that none of the specimens lost hair or suffered permanent injuries from exposure to primary cosmic radiation, except that black rats incurred some damage to hair-follicle pigment cells, causing the affected cells to produce white hair. This was the only experiment that indicated that a test subject had been affected by exposure to cosmic radiation.

There were no results from the experiments indicating that cosmic radiation has any biological effect that cannot be explained on the basis of available physical descriptions of radiations at these altitudes. None of the experiments evaluating physical and mental functions showed adverse conditions as a result of being exposed to cosmic rays.

The question of possible genetic damage caused by cosmic radiation is also vitally important. Dr. H. J. Muller of Indiana University, who was awarded the Nobel prize for his work in radiobiology, has analyzed the genetic hazards that could possibly be expected from cosmic radiation in space. His findings for man are encouraging. In previous studies of genetic damage caused by radiations, he has shown that single high-energy particles have a much smaller effect than diffuse radiations such as X rays and gamma rays. The cosmic-ray particles do harm, if any, to the individual rather than to his children. It is expected, therefore, that cosmic rays will have no demonstrable genetic effects, even if space crews should be exposed in their satelloids for extended periods of time. Dr. Muller believes that the risks the space pilot will run in this respect will be many times less than those that people take when they handle X-ray machines carelessly. But we shall not get the complete answer to the question until we undertake experimental flights with humans.

Solar radiations and ultraviolet rays, capable of grilling the crews of rocket craft, comprise more space hurdles that must be cleared. The Sun emits some of its rays in great bursts, but the Earth's atmosphere filters out nearly all of them. In space, however, the ultraviolet eruptions would hit our satellites and space vehicles unimpeded. Dr. Heinz Haber says that a vehicle's metal walls will shield the crew, but that the cockpit windows must also be protected. Transparent materials that absorb ultraviolet rays are available, but panes of glass or plastic cannot withstand massive showers of such radiations without becoming discolored, muddy, and finally useless as windows. It might be necessary to have covers of some type, which can be kept closed in full sunshine and opened only for purposes of observation.

There is another reason why covers will be required. If the pilot looks out of a cockpit window viewing space, the blue of the skies will have given way to deep blackness. Together with the atmosphere the soft light of day will have vanished, and close to the blinding metallic disk of the Sun will be perceived the stars of the Milky Way. It is difficult to visualize what this unearthly marriage of day and night will look like. The razor-sharp contrasts between blinding light and utter blackness will be extremely hard on the pilot's eyes. Disturbing afterimages caused by the Sun and the sunlit parts of the ship's structure will occur when his eyes are turned away from the window.

The amount of acceleration a human can cope with depends upon two factors, the direction of gravity's pull relative to the body, and the time period over which it acts. Small amounts of acceleration over a prolonged period affect the internal organs and can result in permanent physiological damage. Large values of acceleration applied for even a fraction of a second, such as a decelerative jolt, can affect the skeletal structure.

How much acceleration will the space pilot be subject to? To find a partial answer to that question, scientists at the Wright Air Development Center in Dayton, Ohio, have calculated the acceleration curves of a three-stage orbital satelloid. They found that to attain orbital velocity, a vehicle would have to experience accelerations ranging from 3 g's for ten minutes to 10 g's for approximately two minutes. A body under 1-g's acceleration has its normal weight; for more than 1-g's acceleration, the body's weight is increased proportionately. Recently released findings of such tests conducted by the Navy indicate that a normal healthy adult in the *supine*, or face-up, position can withstand chest-to-back acceleration forces of 15 $g's$ for five seconds with no indication of impending blackout. Nevertheless, pain in the chest and difficulty in breathing are experienced.

It appears probable that the satelloid pilot will be in a supine position during periods of acceleration. The former director of Navy's Aviation Medical Acceleration Laboratory, Captain C. F. Gell, visualizes space craft of the near future with the pilot traveling to the outer regions of space "following the rim of the Earth's atmospheric belt for 10,000 or 20,000 miles and returning to Earth, all in a few hours." He recommends supinating the crew during upward acceleration or downward decelerations, and allowing the men to resume the seated position in straight-line flight. This way the crew will be maximally protected against acceleration stresses at all times. The Navy has had a working model of a supinating seat for some time now. Normally, the pilot sits upright, as he would in a conventional aircraft seat. As acceleration increases the seat slips down and the pilot leans back into a nearly horizontal position, but still in control of his aircraft.

Among aeromedical scientists there is a difference of opinion about whether the *prone,* or face-down, position is better than the supine. Advocates of the prone position say that a supinated pilot would have difficulty controlling his ship, and that the prone is the more natural position. As a matter of interest, the Wright Brothers did their first flying in the prone position. But those men championing the supine position say that the prone position is uncomfortable for long periods of time and exposes the pilot more severely to positive and negative $g's$.

More recently, scientists at the Wright Air Development Center made tests with their human centrifuge to determine whether a man inside a three-stage rocket could adequately perform a tracking task while the rocket engine was accelerating the craft upward; also they tried to learn whether a man could respond to a sudden emergency with an appropriate sequence of actions.

For the test, the subject sat in the centrifuge in an approximately conventional seated position with respect to the line of flight. His back was raised 20 degrees from the horizontal plane, and his legs 65 degrees. With a short "joy stick" on the floor within easy reach, he was to maintain in a given position the needles of two indicators suspended in front of him. During the run the centrifuge simulated the varying accelerations of a three-stage rocket, with corresponding peaks of 8, 5.8 and 5.8 g's over a six-minute period.

Air Force scientists found that although the subject could move his wrist freely to control the stick, he could control only one needle while allowing the other to wander. Nonetheless, they felt that manual control of a three-stage rocket vehicle, such as von Braun's design, is within the realm of possibility. Summing up the tests, the scientists said, "The studies indicate that a trained operator of an orbital rocket or intercontinental ballistic missile could do more than merely endure the accelerations while automatic computers took over the task of adjusting it accurately to a predetermined course."

Before taking off on an actual flight, space pilots must be thoroughly indoctrinated in a human centrifuge. This would not only familiarize them with the physical sensations involved, but also allay any apprehensions they might have.

A similar opinion has been expressed by the director of the Navy's Aviation Medical Acceleration Laboratory, Captain H. G. Shepler. He is convinced that with proper indoctrination and training, an individual can probably somewhat increase his ability to withstand accelerative forces. For instance, after a test when the subject becomes experienced and knows how to strain-tighten his abdominal muscles, he can increase his tolerance to positive g's.

From the studies on human tolerance to acceleration there seems to be ample experimental evidence indicating that normal human males in either the prone or supine position can tolerate an accelerative force of as much as 7 g's for ten minutes or more, while forces up to 10 g's can be tolerated for as long as 100 seconds. It is doubtful if these values will be exceeded by a satelloid craft either in take-off or landing, and it therefore appears that intolerable accelerative forces will not be encountered by tomorrow's space pilots.

Once a satelloid has attained orbital velocity and the rocket engines are shut off, the crew will be in a gravity-free state. No animal or man has yet been in this condition for more than a few seconds at a time, and it is therefore impossible to predict all the objective and subjective effects of such a condition. In the summer of 1951 a series of jet flights designed to expose a pilot and passenger to periods of essentially zero gravity was accomplished through the use of a *Shooting Star* fighter. The aircraft was modified for a prone-position bed to be installed into the nose extension. This ship could be flown from the bed or from the conventional cockpit seat. The craft at full throttle in level or slightly descending flight, having reached a constant velocity, was abruptly pulled up into an attitude vertical to the ground. At this point the power was reduced so that the craft described a ballistic, rocketlike trajectory, decelerating as it ascended, reaching zenith, and then accelerating in its descent at the rate of 32 feet per second per second. While a rocket like the *Aerobee* begins its zero-g flight at a velocity of one mile per second, the jet entered this zero-g pattern at about ⅙ that velocity. Hence, while the *Aerobee* rocket gives a three- to four-minute zero-g period, the *Shooting Star* gave only 15 to 25 seconds. Both the pilot and the passenger were instrumented to obtain heart rates and electrocardiograms. The pilot's compartment was instrumented with accelerometers in three axes. During each flight, the subjects were given eight to ten sub-gravity runs that averaged 15 seconds' duration.

The findings, as reported by Dr. E. R. Ballinger, of the Aero Medical Laboratory, indicated that as long as the subject was held firmly in place by his safety belt and had a point of visual reference, he was, with moderate effort, able to maintain his sense of orientation. However, it was the opinion of the participants that had they been unrestrained and blindfolded, disorientation might have been extreme. Co-ordination was unimpaired. The mild tendency to overreach could easily be controlled by looking at the object of the reaching maneuver. There were no significant alterations in heart rates or electrocardiograms during any of the runs. Thirty zero-gravity runs averaging 15 seconds each gave no suggestion of motion sickness, vertigo or in-co-ordination attributable to the subgravity state.

The evidence at hand seems to indicate that no serious consequences will result from exposure to the gravity-free state. The worst that might happen, apparently, would be an inability in orienting oneself and the occurrence of perhaps a mild form of motion sickness.

The walls of a rocket ship will be able to ward off only fine meteoric dust as even small meteors, the size of pinheads, could easily puncture the walls of the ship. The tremendous energy of a meteor will immediately be transformed into heat at the point of impact, and will cause vaporization of the steel to a greater or lesser degree, depending on the size of the meteor. This action will be followed by a minor explosion, for the point of impact will absorb almost the total energy of the meteor.

A number of investigators, including Haber, believe that the chance of collision is great enough to cause alarm. Extensive studies of the meteor problem have also been made by Fred L. Whipple. For the last 15 years Dr. Whipple has been photographing meteors and measuring how they burn away by friction in the upper atmosphere. He has calculated that an artificial satellite or a space platform would be punctured by a meteor about twice a month, although later information indicates that it might be as seldom as twice a year.

It is probable that the holes made by most meteors will be small enough so that the air would take some time to escape from the interior, but these minutes of grace offer no real security. Even though bells and flashing lights might warn the crew in time for them to put on oxygen masks, and even though an emergency pressurization system might automatically be put to use before air pressure becomes dangerously low, we presume the loss in pressure might call for an emergency return to Earth.

The meteor bumper, which consists of a thin secondary wall placed an inch or so outside the main wall of a satellite or space craft, might be useful. The bumper would not completely stop the meteors, but they would shatter on it, leaving the inner wall unpunctured. Only small fragments and debris would hit the actual shell, and these would be distributed over a large area. If properly constructed of heavy enough materials, the meteor bumper could reduce the hazard considerably, stopping most small meteors. But additional weight is almost disastrous for the design of any space vehicle. Protection could be gained by having automatic plugging devices, similar in principle to the Air Force's self-sealing fuel tanks.

When discussing the possibility of traveling to the Moon, people often say that they would not mind such a voyage—provided they were guaranteed a return trip. It is common now to accept the idea that we soon shall be sending space vehicles aloft, and it is equally common to hear people ask how these ships or satelloids will be brought back to Earth safely. Indeed, the *re-entry* problem, return at high speeds from space into the atmosphere, has long been considered the most dangerous maneuver that any vehicle could possibly attempt. While take-off and ascent to an orbit probably will be

controlled automatically from the ground base, the pilot might have
to handle the return flight to Earth.

It takes large amounts of propellants to put a satelloid or satellite-
type craft into an orbit. During burning of these propellants, including those of booster stages, if any, a large portion of the chemical
energy is converted into kinetic energy. This is transferred to the
final stage. If this last stage, or the actual craft, remains outside of
the atmosphere, its kinetic energy changes very little. In space it is
not apparent in any dramatic way, except that the crew is aware that
the ship is moving around the Earth at a high speed. But as soon as
the returning ship reaches the atmosphere again, the kinetic energy,
which was paid for so dearly in propellants during the ascent, mani-
fests itself in a speed of about 18,000 miles per hour relative to an
atmosphere at rest.

Consequently, all the energy developed in the ascent of a space
vehicle must be eliminated during the return glide. At this point, a
question appears. Would it not be simpler to reduce the excessive
speed with a counterblast of rocket motors? The answer is a simple
one. It would take an excessive amount of propellants to reduce the
speed. And since these propellants would have to be brought up to
the orbit initially, such a rocket ship, when taking off from the Earth,
would require at least four or five stages and would probably stand
as high as the Empire State Building. It follows that we must rule
out the use of rocket counterblasts to slow down the returning craft;
we must utilize the resistance offered freely to us by the atmosphere.

The details of a *re-entry glide* from an orbit outside the Earth's
atmosphere have been studied intensively. There is agreement that
skin friction will not be high enough to cause the ship to disintegrate.
However, the descent of a ship through the upper atmosphere will
be so fast that air friction will heat the outer metal skin of body and
wings to a temperature of about 1,300 degrees Fahrenheit, and the
ship will turn in color from steel blue to cherry red. Yet there is no
reason for undue concern, inasmuch as heat-resistant steels that can
endure such temperatures are already available. The cockpit canopy
might be made of double-paned glass with a liquid coolant flowing
between the panes. The crew will be properly heat-insulated and
cooled by means of the refrigerator-type air-conditioning system.

About 50 miles above the Earth, due to the downward gravity-
powered swing from the orbit, the velocity will increase somewhat

even though there is already considerable air resistance at this altitude. The wings do not give aerodynamic lift, but they can be used to prevent the craft from soaring out of the atmosphere and back into space again. The pilot will push his control stick forward and force the ship to stay at an altitude of exactly 50 miles. The air resistance gradually slows the vehicle and only then can the actual descent into the denser atmosphere begin. From there on, the wings bear more and more of the weight, and after a distance of about 10,000 miles in the atmosphere, the velocity will be down to less than 6,000 miles per hour. By this time, the ship will have descended to a height of about 30 miles.

At a point 15 miles above the Earth, the returning craft will slow down to the speed of sound, roughly 750 miles per hour at that altitude. From here on, the craft behaves like a normal airplane. It can land with conventional landing gears. Von Braun suggests that if the runway is missed during the first attempt, a small auxiliary rocket motor might enable the pilot to make a second approach.

There is a significant difference between bringing down a satelloid and a satellite. In comparing the re-entry of the two, Krafft Ehricke points out that a manned satellite, which returns along an elliptic path, as a glider, must follow the more complicated maneuver of first slowing itself down. The satelloid would have started from an orbit in which power is already used. Re-entry maneuvers for the satellite glider appear fairly straightforward if computed under optimistic assumptions, such as correct path, extremely accurate guidance and control system, no atmospheric changes with latitude and no change in aerodynamic coefficients due to thermal stresses caused by the transient aerodynamic heating. A closer study of the descent-from-space problem indicates that a short period of satelloid-type operation can provide a desirable cushion between re-entry and final descent; it increases the safety and reliability of the return operation as well as permits a reorientation with respect to the surface and with respect to desirable landing areas.

ONR admits that the speed of the Douglas satelloid-type craft, as it falls through the vanishing thin air, will rise enough to generate dangerous frictional heat, especially when the air thickens at 10 miles. The leading edges of the stubby wings will glow, and part of their substance will be washed away, even if they are made of heat-resistant metal. But the heating will continue for only a short time, and ONR believes that wings can be made to survive it.

Once in the lower atmosphere, the ship, which has a 20-minute operational flight time, will slow down by circling and will head for a landing field with a very long runway. The ship will touch at 250 miles per hour, and may use a drag parachute to check its speed on the ground. When the pilot steps out and walks away, he will have lived through the longest 20 minutes in the history of manned flight.

Test flights of the satelloid-type Douglas and North American experimental craft will bring us a greater understanding of what we must face in the high-speed rocket-ship glide from a space orbit. Such test flights will furnish valuable information on heat transfer at extreme supersonic speeds. They will tell us how to master the construction techniques and the engineering tasks and show us how to return safely to Earth from flights at the fringes of our atmosphere and from space. They will also encourage us to accept cosmic flight as a routine operation, to advance deeper into interplanetary space, and to build space stations that will give us permanent, manned laboratories and observation posts in the sky.

13. East of the Sun, West of the Moon

About a quarter of a century ago, an airplane piloted by two courageous pioneers was struggling to climb over the wild Alaskan mountains—dark with virgin fir on their lower slopes, and rocky, forbidding and cold at the tops. The aircraft and its crew had one week of continuous flying behind them. With its single engine, which usually ran hesitatingly at high altitudes, the airplane caught a relieving tail wind, which pushed the plane to Edmonton, Canada, ten hours after take-off from Fairbanks. The following day, after another 14 hours of flying, *Winnie Mae* and its two worn-out pilots, Wiley Post and Harold Gatty, landed safely in New York. In one of the wildest receptions New York City had ever given returning heroes, Post and Gatty made their way through a shower of ticker tape to City Hall to be greeted by the mayor. Even the President of the United States, Herbert Hoover, insisted on meeting the heroes to congratulate them on their astounding feat. Wiley Post and Harold Gatty had flown around the world in eight days.

Of course, we would not be surprised if the President of the United States would want to meet and congratulate the young test pilot who will take the first satelloid around the world in 80 minutes. But this pilot is not likely to ride up Broadway right after landing. He will land on the flat Muroc Lake desert in California. He will then be rushed to headquarters for medical checkups and for interviews with scientific and military researchers.

When Lindbergh flew across the Atlantic, or when Post and Gatty flew around the globe in eight days, the world was amazed for weeks. But not so today. What we used to term the remarkable advances in science are not so remarkable any more.

Until recently, modern man has not been very modern. Great men like Da Vinci, Galileo, Newton, Faraday and many others who by virtue of their greatness were modern spoke to an unresponsive world. Bold ideas and revolutionary thoughts that suggested sweeping and sudden changes met with stern resistance. The history of civilization is a study of a long drawn-out process of man's gradual and reluctant acceptance of the fruits of his own genius.

But today, advances in science and progress in all technical fields have been accepted naturally, unflinchingly, without summoning up chimeras or bugbears in the imagination of man. The fantasies and the Jules Verne fictions, many of which science has converted into fact, are today grasped by man and are put into practical use.

While modern man can visualize the horrors implicit in rocket warfare, he is not afraid to delve deeper into the mysteries of rocket science. He does not seek the security of more familiar, more natural realms as did the ancient sailors who hugged the shores to avoid being blown off the edge of the Earth by Boreas, the north wind.

This means that man is determined that the development of rocket science will not hit a ceiling. It means that he is releasing himself in free flights of scientific research, that he is uninhibited, and is ready to ignore any traditional concepts that may be a barrier to space flight. In brief, he is more prepared to live with and to profit by the new geographic and geophysical premises that will undoubtedly be created by this new era.

This is an innovation for man, this idea of embracing an entirely new science that suggests a repatterning of his way of life. In all history, it has never been so. Man has made many valiant thrusts into the unknown, but seldom in the past have contemporaries of dauntless adventurers been enlightened generally or immediately by the brazen announcements of discoveries such as are expected in the area of space flight.

It is significant that the men behind the manned satelloid and space-platform designs—men like Professor Hermann Oberth, Dr. Wernher von Braun, Krafft A. Ehricke, Kurt Stehling and others—are the men in charge of some of our highly advanced guided-missile development. These men are not fiction writers. They are scientists and engineers. They have worked and lived with rockets and missiles for years, they have been repeatedly discouraged by mishaps and failures—yet, these men are the ones who say that manned-satellite platforms can be built. These men are only a few of the many.

Even though we cannot draw an accurate picture of what the first manned satellites will look like, we have reason to believe that many of the ideas suggested by today's designers will be incorporated into them. There is, for example, only one way to create artificial gravity for the crew members—by the use of centrifugal force obtained by spinning a disk or wheel. The cheapest way of generating power in weatherless space is by the use of solar mirrors. We know that for humans there is no substitute for oxygen, and, of course, in space they need pressurized quarters and cabins. Consequently, we must put artificial gravity, air-conditioning, and pressurization systems into the manned space observatories.

The matter of illumination and visibility both inside and outside a satellite must be given serious consideration. In this case, it is interesting to note that test pilots that have flown to altitudes as high as 17 miles report that visibility was not noticeably changed. These pilots say that they were able to orient themselves by reference to the horizon and to recognize geographical landmarks on the surface of the Earth, such as mountain ranges and deserts. However, it has been predicted that light inside the cockpit at satellite altitudes will produce strong contrasts due to the lack of an atmosphere to diffuse the light.

These parameters will determine the design of tomorrow's space satellites to some extent. But the gain in tomorrow's technology might give us new aspects and new ideas that will influence the over-all construction.

The most famous of all manned satellite concepts is von Braun's *Pinwheel Space Station*. This project calls for a satellite built in the shape of an enormous wheel that rotates slowly around its axis. Within its rim, this rotation will generate a centrifugal force sufficient to simulate the effects of gravity, thereby rendering life far more comfortable for the occupants than if they were exposed for extended periods to weightlessness. The satellite will be designed and built in segments of nylon-reinforced plastic. One or more segments will be loaded into a rocket craft in uninflated condition, much as rubber life rafts are loaded and carried by airplanes. Men in pressure suits or in individual, solid-walled cylinders will assemble the

segments in the orbit. When the wheel is complete, it will be inflated
from air tanks. Of course, the satellite will have its own air-conditioning system that will renew the oxygen consumed by the crew and
fulfill the other requirements necessary to provide them with an
ample supply of breathable air. For this purpose, there will be a
periodic visit to the satellite by a rocket craft to provide not only
oxygen or air but also food, water and other necessities. Temperature
control of the interior of the space station may be obtained by regulating the ratio between heat absorption from the Sun and heat
radiation into space. Electric power for the satellite is drawn from a
solar reflector, which generates steam in a boiler tube connected to a
turbine generator. Further, von Braun calculates that a satellite 250
feet in diameter can accommodate a crew of about 200 to 300 men.
The high-flying observatory will weigh 400 tons and can be set up in
the course of 12 to 14 rocket flights to the orbit.

Darrell C. Romick's manned satellite design is even more daring
than von Braun's. An engineer with Goodyear Aircraft Corporation,
Romick has shown the construction of a satellite station with a three
billion cubic foot volume. This is 1,000 times the size of the *Graf
Zeppelin* airship. The Romick satellite is established in an orbit about
the Earth by large satellite ferry rockets that carry crew members
and hardware to the steadily growing orbital satellite. The first two
ferry vessels used are not returned to Earth, but form the embryo of
the station structure.

Romick estimates that it would take three years to complete the
construction. His gigantic satellite is cylindrically shaped. A large
rotating wheel is mounted at one end of the station to provide quarters where crew members can live under artificial gravity conditions provided by the wheel's rotation. The cylindrical segment of
Romick's space satellite is 1,000 feet in diameter and 3,000 feet
long; the wheel is 1,500 feet in diameter and 40 feet thick.

It is possible to outline how man will live in a space station and
what kind of equipment will go into the manned space satellites. The
inhabitants of a space station will not experience day and night in
terms of about 12 hours of light and 12 hours of darkness. The orbital
velocity 320 miles from Earth speeds the satellite around the planet
15 times every 24 hours. One rotation will take one hour and 36 minutes. During this period, the Earth will come directly between the
satellite and the Sun for a 24-minute period, during which time the

station will travel in darkness. The crew will have daylight for one hour and 12 minutes and a brief night of only 24 minutes. During the night period while the inhabitants experience the Earth eclipse, the solar mirror will not absorb energy from the Sun. Consequently, the satellite must be equipped to accumulate the energy that is absorbed during the daytime and store this energy in batteries.

Depending upon the size of the satellite and the scope of its utilization, the station will be equipped with all types of laboratories for physicists and chemical engineers, and with observatories for the astronomers, meteorologists and technicians who will handle the radio and television relay. It is likely that the first manned space satellites will also have one or more military observers aboard, and if the station is built as a military weapons system only, the satellite will contain mainly radar tracking equipment, radio communications gear, and weapons. It is not possible to visualize how effectively the military will be able to use a weapon-equipped satellite.

It is by far more pleasant to speculate on the peaceful missions of the newly inhabited moons. We know that our scientists will value a manned space station as a great advancement. In fact, for many scientists a manned space satellite will revolutionize their research methods. In particular, we feel that one of the most potent utility aspects is that of using the space station as a launching platform for interplanetary voyages. To realize a trip to Mars or Venus with current propellants is a tremendous task if the spaceship is to take off directly from Earth. Such a vehicle would have to be gigantic, and so would the cost of the project. The trouble with rocket flight into the faraway regions of our solar system is that interplanetary filling stations are few and far between. In fact, even among space-travel enthusiasts, there is a widely held belief that trips to the planets with ordinary liquid-fuel rocket ships involve such large quantities of propellants that the technical feasibility of such trips must be questioned.

However, if a rocket ship destined for the Moon or one of the neighbor planets can be launched from an already existing platform outside the Earth's atmosphere, then our greatest problems will be easily solved. The space platform is already traveling at a velocity of 18,000 miles per hour. This speed is given to us free, and we shall need only an additional 7,000 miles per hour to reach the Earth's escape velocity.

If we were to send a manned expedition to the Moon, the advantages we shall have by using a satellite platform as a launching site are obvious. We may assume that a lunar ship will be built in several segments on Earth. These segments will then be brought up to an existing space satellite station by ferry rockets and assembled over a period of time. All preliminary work, such as design, fitting and testing of components will take place on Earth. When the ship is completed, the crew members will be brought up to the satellite, and man's first try for the Moon will be attempted.

The Moon ship will need an engine powerful enough to give the ship a velocity of 7,000 miles per hour for take-off from the space station, and the other engine, plus 5,300 miles per hour of thrust for landing on the Moon. The same amounts of power will be needed for the return trip from the Moon to the space station. If we add up these velocities, we find that a rocket engine must be capable of developing 24,600 miles per hour. It might be that a Moon ship will need power from time to time during the voyage, in order to perform corrective maneuvers. For this purpose, we might want to bring some extra propellants with us, perhaps enough for a velocity increment of 5,400 miles per hour. Even so, the rocket engine requires power to yield a total velocity of only 30,000 miles per hour. In comparison, if we were to travel directly from the Earth to the Moon, our ship would require enough propellants to give a total velocity of more than 75,000 miles per hour. Furthermore, the minimum velocity requirement for escape from Earth is 25,000 miles per hour. The speed of a *Viking* rocket was only 4,000 miles per hour. We also recall that it takes a 70-foot, three-stage rocket weighing more than 20,000 pounds to get a 21.5-pound satellite into an 18,000-miles-per-hour orbit. It is therefore obvious that an already established space platform will be useful for trips not only to the Moon but also to the planets.

A trip to the Moon is, of course, much simpler than a trip to a neighboring planet (even if we ignore the vast differences in distances involved), because the Earth, the Moon, and the spaceship are all subjected to the pull of the Sun in the same manner. All move with approximately the same velocity and, within narrow limits, in the same direction. For this reason the Sun's gravity can be ignored. Therefore the Moon will probably be the goal of the first attempted rocket flight to another body in our solar system.

As for other trips, the planets Jupiter, Saturn, Neptune, Uranus and Pluto are cold enough to liquefy air, and Mercury, closest to the Sun, has temperatures hot enough to melt lead. Consequently these inhospitable planets can be scratched off any contemplated interplanetary flight list during the younger stages of interplanetary exploration.

Venus is 25 million miles from Earth at its closest point, and has temperatures ranging from –15 to 212 degrees Fahrenheit. The dense atmosphere reveals an oxygen content less than a thousandth of that existing over an equal area of the Earth. However, it could be that more oxygen exists nearer the planet's surface.

Venus and Earth are at their closest points only once every 470 days. Since Venus is traveling at 79,000 miles per hour and the Earth at 67,000 miles per hour, the rocket would have to leave Earth well in advance of the time when the planets are at their closest point. Dr. Walter Hohmann, a pioneer of interplanetary studies, estimates that it would take 146 days to go to Venus, a wait of 470 days for a position favorable for departure to Earth, and another 146 days for the trip back.

That fabled planet, Mars, is approximately 35 million miles from Earth at its nearest point. The time needed for an expedition to Mars is two years and 239 days, if we were to use conventional rocket power.

Before we reach the point when we shall be able to build a manned satellite—unless such a project will be undertaken as a crash program within the next few years—it could be that those of our scientists who are working on new propulsion systems will come up with an engine or a power concept that will revolutionize space flight. It did not take many years for our scientists to develop nuclear-power reactors for submarines. Could it be that these same scientists will surprise us and offer us a *nuclear rocket?*

The ancient Greeks gave civilization a big boost by assuming that all things can be comprehensible to all men and that the accumulation of knowledge will eventually vanquish all the mysteries of the universe. It was a Greek, Democritus, who in the fourth century B.C. conjured an atomic theory of matter and gave us the word *atom*, which has been derived from the Greek word meaning "noncuttable." Democritus approached his theory as a philosopher and it was not until the early nineteenth century that experiments by John Dalton, an English chemist, established the scientific theory of atomic structure.

As early as 120 B.C., in Alexandria, Egypt, a young engineer named Hero invented a jet engine which he called an *aeolipile*. It was an effective engine too and was used to open and shut automatically the door to a temple, a feat that Hero's contemporaries must have attributed to an act of the gods and not to mechanical ingenuity.

But despite this successful demonstration, this very simple and practical form of power lay unused for more than 2,000 years. Even the rocket, the oldest and probably the very simplest form of propulsion, was ignored while nineteenth-century man concentrated on one of the most complicated of power-plant mechanisms, the reciprocating or piston engine.

It is interesting that so much of this knowledge winnowed by the liberal thinking of ancients gathered dust on library shelves until the twentieth century when it was stirred into action by the catalytic minds of curious and wondering men who compressed more progress and achievement in a few short years than civilization had experienced in centuries.

Within the span of one man's adult life, aviation was catapulted from a blind speculation to a gigantic reality in world affairs. The tremendous energies of the atomic nucleus were released only forty years after a day when the very existence of the nucleus was unknown. And as progress continued, the time required to complete each step became less and less. The gas-turbine engine burgeoned as a dominating power plant in just a fraction of the time it took to perfect the basic theories of flight. Atomic power was harnessed as a source of motivation almost overnight.

Applying atomic energy to rocket propulsion will challenge the ingenuity of rocket engineers. Although an atomic reactor provides a source of high temperature, it does not afford any mass that can be ejected to the rear and drive the rocket on its path. Therefore, to utilize atomic energy in a rocket, it is necessary to carry extra mass. This might be in the form of tanks of water which, after being converted to steam in a passage through the reactor, would serve to propel the projectile.

Clifford Mannal, General Electric physicist, says that if a rocket must carry water, it might equally well carry other liquids instead, which weigh about as much as water but which, on mixture, will give gaseous products at high temperature. With such a liquid, the advocates of atomic rockets might increase the high temperatures available through the use of nuclear fuels. However, Mannal says, if we can already make a gaseous stream reach a higher temperature than we can contain, the ability of an atomic fuel to raise the temperature of the exit stream without limit, beyond the point where it does us any good, gains us very little.

Considered on the basis of horsepower per pound of weight of the power plant, which is an important index of the efficiency of naval vessels and a dominating number in aircraft propulsion, atomic power does not seem too hopeful a drive for rockets. However, these discouraging observations on the relation of nuclear power to rocket propulsion should not be viewed as insuperable obstacles, but rather as challenges to the enthusiasm and ingenuity of a dedicated group which has already conquered much.

A more likely technique to obtain thrust for the rocket might require the use of a nuclear-*fusion* reactor, which uses the principle of the H-bomb, in which heavy isotopes of the lighter elements such as hydrogen or lithium are applied instead of the conventional uranium. But since the thermonuclear reactor generates heat at about the temperature of the Sun, problems of containment are formidable. One scientist, however, seems to think that these problems will be solved in the not too distant future. He is Eugen Sänger, who has become world-famous for his *photonic* rocket concept.

The photonic rocket is propelled by the reactive force of a vast stream of "light" particles erupting from the rocket's nozzles. The source of the photons is a small hydrogen-fission pile often referred to as a man-made star.

The photons of a light beam possess no mass at rest. However, they do have an inert mass; when a photon hits a wall, the photon exercises an impulse upon the wall. Such impacts of a great number of photons present a light pressure upon the wall. Likewise, light pressure is acting upon the reflector of a searchlight. If light pressure should become high enough, it could be made to act like the exhaust stream of a rocket, the function of the exhaust gases being replaced by the oriented light beam.

Dr. Sänger has calculated the effect and designed the most important components of such a rocket, which are a *photonic source* of
extremely high intensity and a reflector for the proper orientation of
the photons into one common beam.

The intensity of a given source of radiation is known. It increases
with the temperature rather rapidly. But it achieves a propulsive
effect only when very high temperature values are reached. Hence,
in the application of photonic rockets, it is necessary to achieve these
extremely high temperatures in the photonic source. These temperatures can be obtained only through nuclear reaction.

Dr. Sänger calls the photonic source a *nuclear lamp*. The processes
in a photonic rocket involve heating a gas to extremely high temperatures by means of a stationary nuclear reactor; whereby in this way,
a radiation of high intensity results together with the orientation of
the radiation through a reflector, and acceleration of the exhaust. The
production of thrust results primarily through radiation pressure and
to a smaller extent through gas pressure. In the case of photonic
rockets, the medium for propulsion, the stream of photons which
have high pressure effect is amplified in vacuum or at altitudes beyond atmospheric.

Flight velocities approaching the speed of light may be expected
for photonic rockets, according to Dr. Sänger. But other somewhat
more feasible atomic propulsion developments are being studied,
and it seems that some of these will eliminate the need for the fantastic temperatures encountered with photonic rockets. This might
be the reason why most atomic rocket research seems to be applied
to these power regimes rather than to the photonic.

The *ion* rocket has been suggested. The British rocket expert, Dr.
J. H. Fremlin, looks forward to the time when giant spaceships may
be making interstellar voyages. Several years ago, Dr. Fremlin described what has been called a hypothetical gaseous reactor which
would use gaseous deuterium as fuel. The reactor was to be housed
in a gigantic steel sphere. Its power output would be in the region of
30 million kilowatts. The reactor itself could be used directly as a
rocket, ejecting the reaction products in a jet.

A more conservative concept—although based upon a similar principle—has been suggested by the Redstone missile engineer, Dr.
Ernst Stuhlinger. His *electrical propulsion system* produces thrust by
expelling ions and electrons instead of combustion gases. A nuclear

reactor provides the primary power for a turboelectric generator, and the electric power then accelerates the ions. Cesium or rubidium are the best fuels available, according to Stuhlinger, because of their high atomic mass and low ionization energy. (We recall that the greater the mass of the exhaust gas for a given velocity, the higher the rocket's forward speed.) Introduced into a ceramic propulsion chamber, the cesium or rubidium atoms strike a grid of incandescent platinum plates. The platinum absorbs the outermost electrons, leaving positively charged ions that pass through the grid into a thrust chamber. Here, the ion stream is accelerated to extremely high velocities by negatively charged electrodes around the chamber's nozzle and is discharged in the form of an electrical jet exhaust.

An electrical spaceship with 150 tons' pay load and an almost insignificant initial acceleration would be traveling to Mars and back in a total travel time of about two years. The ship would have a take-off mass of 730 tons.

One significant difference between electrically propelled spaceships and ships using conventional liquid propellants is that electrical ships require a special power source to provide power for the ion acceleration. Since an electrical propulsion system develops only a relatively small thrust, the system will stay in operation during the whole flight.

There are many technical difficulties involved in designing and building such a spaceship, and we know of no attempt to realize such plans in the near future. On the other side, at least one aircraft company in the United States is said to have been awarded a study contract for electrical rocket propulsion, and another company is studying photonic rockets.

Someday man might step aboard an entirely different kind of interplanetary ship. This vehicle will not be rocket propelled, yet it will employ atomic power.

Engineers and physicists are closing in on the development of what is referred to as *antigravity propulsion*. This is a system based upon the counteracting of Earth's gravity. If it had not been for the gravitational pull of the Earth, we would, of course, be thrown into space because of the centrifugal force caused by the Earth's 1,000-mile-per-hour equatorial rotation. Thus, if we can control the Earth's gravity pull as we control the energy output of a combustion engine or of an electric motor, we might be able to travel to other solar systems as easily as we fly on Earth.

For years scientists have been studying gravity. They bracket the phenomenon with life itself as the greatest unsolved mystery in the universe. Now, with combined efforts and funds, our various research institutions, aircraft manufacturers and the Department of Defense have launched an over-all attack on the problem.

The Gravity Research Foundation, operated in connection with the Sir Isaac Newton Library of the Babson Institute in New Boston, New Hampshire, has spent thousands of dollars and manhours studying gravity. Other centers where gravity research is now in progress include the Institute for Advanced Study at Princeton, New Jersey, the University of North Carolina, the University of Indiana's School of Advanced Mathematical Studies, and the Purdue University Research Foundation.

Scientists all over the world have done a great deal of work on electrical and magnetic phenomena. England's great scientist, Michael Faraday, while making an experiment, uncovered what might be a connection between electricity and gravity, and he spent much time and effort to produce a direct lifting force from gravity by using electrical energy. Faraday paved the way for construction of electromagnets.

In modern physics, the connection between electromagnetism and gravity is believed to be the clue to the problem—and atomic power may help us put the theory to work. Dr. Stanley Deser and Dr. Richard Arnowitt of the Institute of Advanced Study at Princeton believe that the recently discovered nuclear and subnuclear particles of high energy, which are difficult to explain by any present-day theory, may prove to be the key that will help solve the problem. It is their suggestion that the new particles may prove to be basic gravitational energy that is being converted continually and automatically in an expanding universe directly into the most useful nuclear and electromagnetic forms. "One of the most hopeful aspects of the problem," they say, "is that until recently gravitation could be observed but not experimented on in any controlled fashion; while now with the advent in the past two years of the new high-energy accelerators, the Brookhaven *Cosmotron* and the even more recent Berkeley *Bevatron*, the new particles which have been linked with the gravitational field can be examined and worked with at will."

Of course, many scientists insist that they are not supposed to concern themselves with freedom from gravity. Such ideas make exciting material for pulp magazines, but anyone who seriously considers screens for gravity is tilting at windmills. The method of science has always been one of careful observation, generalization and mathematical expression, and then deduction and prediction. A theory to be valid must weigh positive and negative evidence equally well, and its predictions must be found true in subsequent experimentation and observation. The theory must be careful not to indicate anything that is known to be absent. However, in view of the latest developments in research, it appears that scientists are discovering factors necessary for the antigravity propulsion theory. This theory is that of the gravitational field concept.

The *g-field theory* for propulsion is rather simple. Were we to be placed several thousand miles from the Earth's surface, we should fall to the Earth with an increasing velocity. If the mass of the Earth were doubled, so would our rate of acceleration.

It follows that if by some means the mass of the Earth were controllable and alternately increased and decreased, our rate of acceleration would fluctuate accordingly. Also, we would be completely unaware of it because the Earth's gravitational field is acting on every part of our body uniformly, every molecule and every atom at the same instant.

William P. Lear, chairman of the board of Lear, Inc., is known as one of the most enthusiastic researchers in the area of gravity. In 1950 he received the coveted Collier Trophy from the President of the United States. Lear is convinced that it will be possible to create the electrogravitational fields whose polarity can be controlled to cancel out gravity. He says all the mass, materials and human beings within these fields will be part of them. "They will be adjustable so as to increase or decrease the weight of any object in its surroundings. They won't be affected by the Earth's gravity or that of any celestial body. This means that if you were in an antigravitational airplane or spaceship that carried along its own gravitational field— no matter how fast you accelerated or changed course—your body would no more feel it than it now feels the speed of the Earth."

This statement would ordinarily shock an orthodox aeronautical engineer or aerodynamicist, whose basic theory is built on the flow of a liquid (air) over a surface to provide lift. Yet the only reason lift is needed is to overcome gravity. But someday our scientists may move us into the antigravitational age. Just as scientists moved us into the atomic age and then into the hydrogen age, they may find a way to create a gravitational field whose polarity can be controlled to cancel gravity.

If a spaceship is capable of creating its own gravitational field, and if this is controllable, the ship will accelerate as long as the field is there. The acceleration will depend entirely on the strength of the field. With g-field propulsion, a spaceship could be at rest one moment and be traveling at near the speed of light the next instant, and the occupants of the vehicle would be unaware that they had moved.

When we consider a body in space moving toward a planet by its own g-field, while assuming the planet's gravitational effect to be neutralized, another important phenomenon occurs. The body begins to graze the outer tenuous layers of the planet's atmosphere, but the particles nearest to the body will be affected by the g-field and therefore move along with the body itself. The result will be the absence of local friction and therefore no drag. A British gravity researcher, Leonard G. Cramp, suggests that this moving belt of air would impart movement through friction to the air particle outside the effective area of the g-field and there would be air disturbance and therefore noise, but if we consider that the velocity of these particles would become less the farther out they reached, the noise would be greatly cushioned and for that matter probably inaudible from the planet's surface.

An antigravity-propelled spaceship has been visualized in this manner. In the center of the vehicle, which is disk-shaped, is placed an atomic reactor that drives a turbine, which in turn drives a generator. The resulting current is supplied to two coil-shaped electromagnets placed at a distance from each other in parallel planes. The polarity of the resulting magnetic fields is such that an attraction is set up in the coils and the strength of the field is governed only by the energy output of the atomic reactor and the generator.

The upper coil represents Earth and the lower coil the ship itself. When the pilot reverses the polarity, the ship hurtles into space. With such propulsion, it might be possible to fly anywhere, including other solar systems, with almost any desired speed, without the problem of heat barriers, blackouts from great accelerations—and, in all probability, without noise.

In the history of every major development are people of little foresight or courage, eager to point out the difficulties, the uncertainties and the dangers in new and untried ideas. These people are becoming scarce, as the rapid advancement of science is so convincing that only few men will stand up and attempt to disprove speciously the concepts behind ion rockets, photonic propulsion, antigravity and whatever other power regimes might develop in the minds of scientists. Today the theories are farfetched, and tomorrow they are hardware.

The beginning—the launching of satellites carrying instruments and research animals—is an accomplishment in its own right. It promises to bring to the last half of the twentieth century progress even more dramatic than that brought by the airplane during the first half. However, the ventures cannot be accomplished without an upheaval in the use of manpower and an application of human genius, sincerity and willingness.

14. Men Wanted

We are starting on what will certainly be one of the great adventures of man—the exploration of space. We shall go equipped with small instrumented satellites, manned satellites and satelloids, space platforms and physical laboratories. We may use new flight concepts, and new energy and power regimes such as liquid rockets, nuclear-fuel rockets, ion and photon rockets, and possibly antigravity propulsion. On the eve of this adventure all the signs are favorable. Our engineers can provide the hardware, and the amount of money required is not as great as we first thought, and we have as well the overwhelming encouragement of the military and the public.

As a result, our view has changed. We are not asking whether we shall ever penetrate space. Instead, today's questions are: How can the problems of unmanned as well as manned space flight best be approached? What manpower do we have to solve them? What new fields of study will appear? How will they be organized?

With the *Vanguard* program, the United States has already written the prologue to unmanned space flight. After the prologue comes the book which must include analyses of the satellite's data by men in all scientific fields. It must also include descriptions of flights far beyond the Earth's atmosphere and into interplanetary space. These can be unmanned or manned, but in any case the over-all problems will probably be solved on the basis of our present missile programs.

One of America's top rocket scientists, Kurt Stehling, believes that the space flights of the future could get their impetus in one of several ways. It could proceed at a time when military requirements for missiles are reduced, or it could proceed as a multiservice military project parallel with the missile programs. A less likely means would be through the formation of a special agency, such as the Atomic Energy Commission, to promote space flight. Least likely would be a program undertaken by a group of industries or foundations who would bear most or all the financial burden.

These proposals imply space-flight research by individual countries each going their own way. However, a fifth road that seems most probable can come as a result of the United States and other countries putting money and encouragement into the IGY satellite program. From this start, space flight could proceed under the guidance of The International Astronautical Federation and UNESCO, and, finally, UNESCO could be completely responsible for supervising space-flight research and the flights themselves. Since there is no more ambitious program than that of exploring the Universe, it seems unlikely that any one country or any one foundation can provide the necessary money and talent for a venture whose springboard is Earth.

Whom do we have to do the work? What are their qualifications and experience? How will they proceed? Where does the taxpayer fit in?

Studying the questions from the vantage point of a former Canadian, Kurt Stehling assesses the groups involved. He says that the technicians and scientists who were formerly enemy nationals (mostly Germans) and who have come to this country have often been leaders in urging the beginning of a space-flight program. They have shown some remarkable technical aptitudes and experience in the field of rocket propulsion. Many of these men are in positions of trust and responsibility in the missile industry of this country. As such, they influence the functions and details of a space-flight program, but, because of their former national background, and sometimes anomalous positions as citizens, they suffer handicaps when policy decisions must be made. They have a natural inclination for missile projects after having worked for the Nazi war machine for many years. However, they are sometimes not fitted for interpreting the missile program to the American people, and they have to be very careful not to show impatience with our democratic processes and the fine points of good public relations. In brief, the technical influence of these people is considerable, but their political and managerial influence tends to be of a lower order.

The second group of people in the United States who will influence space flights is the existing body of designers, engineers, and managerial personnel who have been in the aircraft business for a long time. Their outlook is definitely less influenced by haste and impatience. They naturally tend to be cautious, especially those who regulate the activity of large defense or industrial plants. However, these managerial and leading technical men will play an important role in guiding and supervising the activities of the younger people who will lead the future space or orbital flight projects.

The third large personnel subdivision may be grouped as the younger engineers and physicists who are just beginning to make a mark in the jet-propulsion and rocket fields. These men tend to be impatient with the objectives of the missile and rocket program, and they often minimize the great technical problems that will be met, although they are not unaware of them. They are not as politically cautious as the older men, and can often outstrip the slow-moving pace of public opinion. Nevertheless, the enthusiasm of this younger group will make its weight increasingly felt with time, and it certainly is to become the most important single technical group in any space-flight program.

The group that posterity will depend upon is composed of the students in school today. These people have not been graven with a pattern of old ideas, nor are they fearful of losing a profession or status they spent many years to get—a loss that many aerodynamicists experienced when flight changed from subsonic to supersonic, and that many electronics engineers experienced when the research picture changed from long-wave to micro-wave investigations.

Part of this academic group consists of the small but growing segment of scholars and teachers who, because of their less compromising positions, can speculate about the various aspects of space flight. They often treat their subject in an objective and penetrating fashion, giving rise to new ideas. This approach is difficult for men in industry who are busy with specific projects.

The most critical group comprises the American voters and taxpayers who must pay the final bill. The preceding groups can do much good by approaching the space-flight subject in a calm manner, and by interpreting the benefits and possibilities of space flight as objectively as possible. It is equally important that the political representatives of the people be fully informed about the economic and diplomatic aspects. Someday the public may be in a severely questioning mood, especially if budget limitations and increasing taxes become more highly disturbing to the country's economy.

It is clear that for the United States to remain dominant on Earth, the country must arrange either in concert, or if necessary, alone, for a commanding position in space. If it does not, it may find itself in the position of a man at the bottom of a deep well, seeing the blue sky far above but despairing of ever reaching it. The opportunity is here, but the National Science Foundation reports that shortages of scientists and engineers impede the research and development programs of many companies whose activities represent a large and critically important segment of the nation's scientific research effort. Interviews with officials of 200 large companies, conducted by the United States Department of Labor's Bureau of Labor Statistics, showed that at least half of these companies are unable to hire enough research scientists and engineers to meet their needs, and one out of every three companies said they have major or substantial shortages of such personnel. The remaining companies interviewed did not report numerical shortages of research personnel, but many emphasized their need for better-qualified scientists and engineers. The 200 companies interviewed employ well over 50 per cent of all scientists and engineers working in industrial research and development today.

The need for additional personnel in the research and development activities of the reporting companies covered a wide range of fields—chemical, electrical, mechanical and aeronautical engineering, chemistry, physics, metallurgy, mathematics and a number of others. The demand for additional scientists and engineers also extended to all levels of training and to new graduates as well as to experienced men, although most company officials said they had a greater need for personnel with experience or advanced degrees than for new graduates with only the bachelor's degree.

Far from decreasing, the present shortage of engineers and scientists in the United States will become worse before it becomes better. Fewer technically trained men are being prepared by the colleges and universities. According to a report by the Teachers College of Columbia University, between the years 1950 and 1954 the total number of students graduated by colleges and universities decreased about 34 per cent, owing in part to the fewer number of students studying under G.I. Bills. The number of natural-science graduates decreased about 51 per cent in the same period and the number of engineering graduates decreased about 58 per cent.

Despite the diminishing supply of technical talent, the fields of space flight may soon be calling for steadily increasing numbers of scientifically trained men. Starting at the time of the IGY, aircraft and allied industries will be bidding to build satellites and satellite components for many specialized space investigations. Later these building programs may be enlarged to include spaceships. Finally, the outstanding engineering companies in the United States may have a great part of their facilities devoted to solving problems of space flight. In addition, there may be many ancillary activities such as spaceship servicing, data interpreting, and space medicine. Yet, as we have seen, the future of space flight depends upon present missile developments, and although unlimited opportunities exist here, today the field is quite underpopulated.

In an *Aero Digest* article, L. L. Waite, vice-president of North American Aviation, writing about employment opportunities, said that development of a missile calls for work in subsonic, transonic and supersonic aerodynamics. It requires that the thermodynamicist confront aerodynamic heating problems. It calls upon the electro-mechanical engineer to design and develop equipment that can automatically control and guide a missile in flight. It demands from still other engineers the development of structural materials that have better high-temperature properties than any materials previously used in conventional aircraft.

No less imposing is the requirement that missile engineers overcome problems arising from the need to subminiaturize electronic components able to withstand greater shock and humidity and temperature extremes than before. Equally important is the demand upon engineering for the design and development of propulsion systems that are able to deliver power of a magnitude greater than ever thought practical. Here the engineering effort involves inquiry into the broad range of various high-thrust engines—jets, ram-jets, rockets, combinations of rockets and jets—along with research and development of the most effective and efficient propellants for the missile's power plant.

Engineers are vitally needed for design and development work in preliminary analysis, aerodynamics, aerothermodynamics, thermodynamics, structures, stress analysis, missile components, systems, and static and flight tests.

Important in the electromechanical engineering program is the size and weight of electronic components. Such components are potted in plastics to make them better able to stand shock, humidity and temperature extremes. In designing and developing electromechanical equipment to control missiles, missile engineers employ some of the finest available computers. They use electromechanical brains to make electromechanical brains.

In advanced electromechanical programs, more engineers are needed for the design of guidance systems, component development, instrumentation, radar systems, computer systems and the development of related systems.

At North American Aviation's Missile and Control Equipment Propulsion Center some of the nation's most advanced work in rocket propulsion is being conducted. An outgrowth of such work was the company's announcement of the development of a 50,000-pound thrust, liquid-propellant rocket engine capable of powering a test sled on rails at speeds exceeding 1,500 miles per hour and reaching that speed from a dead stop in 4.5 seconds.

The prerequisite for a missile engineer is an engineering degree from a recognized engineering school. Experience may be substituted for formal education in some instances, but a degree is a known quantity and is a good starting point. Engineers most desired are those with majors in mechanical, aeronautical, electrical or electronic engineering. Much in demand are mechanical engineers with options in thermodynamics or aeronautics. Civil engineers adapt readily to stress work and design. Chemical engineers find a special niche in thermodynamics studies. Those with engineering physics degrees can be used readily in aerophysics or electromechanical systems projects.

For materials research in connection with airframe and the broad propulsion program, the need is for chemists, physicists, metallurgists, chemical engineers, and welding and ceramics engineers. Graduate aeronautical engineers find that the study of additional courses help them become better-qualified missile engineers and these include the theory of jet propulsion, rockets, turbojets and ramjets, mathematics through the usual requirements for a master's degree, advanced thermodynamics, advanced compressible-flow theory, advanced heat transfer, and fluid dynamics. A course in servomechanisms is valuable background for aeronautical and mechanical engineers.

Graduate engineers just out of school and with no missile experience find themselves welcomed into established groups. Many graduates each year are given informal on-project training and develop into excellent engineers. The best background an engineer can have, of course, is direct missile experience. The experience level determines the starting-salary level. The next most valuable background is work in connection with conventional aircraft engineering. Other related engineering work is design of mechanical, electrical and electronic devices and piping. A background in heat transfer is also quite helpful.

Within the organizations participating in guided-missile research and development, the missile engineer's long-range opportunities are unlimited. In addition, there is the promise of applying guided-missile technology to other enterprises. Such an extension of a missile engineer's experience and ability would parallel the application of a nuclear physicist's talents and experience in atomic energy to such fields as food, medicine, electric-power generation and industrial research. There is good technical promise of applying to industry such developments in missile engineering as heat-resistant materials, subminiaturized electronic components, high-thrust light-weight propulsion systems, chemical milling processes, automatic flight-control systems and instrumentation.

It used to be that a good harbor, or good hunting, or good farming led to an urban development. Now cities are arising where the Earth's rotation is the fastest. Later, other cities will form where they can best satisfy requirements as a depot for the Moon and planets.

We have seen how groups of engineers and technicians are being assigned to various posts such as Patrick Air Force Base and the Bahama Islands in order to assure the success of the launching of the *Vanguard* satellite on a near-equatorial orbit. These men, their wives and children are establishing first communities and then cities. These locations will not be like the towns of the old West, which were deserted when the gold ran out. These are towns being populated by highly educated men and women, some of whom have a dream of making an epochal contribution to science. Epochs do not occur overnight. They have a beginning, such as the satellite, they have a middle, such as space flight, and they have an end, such as the colonizing of various planets. An epoch, too, does not occur without the expenditure of enormous amounts of energy. For a man-made one, tremendous logistic support is needed. Food and transportation must be provided. Workers need homes, theaters, schools and medical facilities. There must be provisions for leisure-time activities. The people must have political representation. All these services and commodities mean jobs—jobs today and for a long time after today for technicians in every field of endeavor. In addition, there will arise thousands of jobs in areas as yet unexplored.

One modern area has already received academic recognition. A first course of study in space techniques was given by Professor Paul Sandorff and his associates in the 1956 spring term at the Massachusetts Institute of Technology. The course was entitled *Orbital Vehicles.* Covered in the study were mechanics of projectiles and orbital vehicles, properties of the upper atmosphere and space, space flight, spaceship power plants, return to Earth, design and structural considerations, instrumentation of satellite vehicles, a hypothetical flight to Mars, and guidance and control of a ferry vehicle. A number of other colleges are starting to follow MIT's lead.

It is not too early then to ask for course outlines and textbooks for the space-flight sciences. Those who expect to go into the field professionally will want to be able to pick out those areas of study especially suited to their interests and talent. Once these areas are defined, they will form the groundwork for preparing suitable reference material, methods of analysis, and other tools needed to support the component sciences. Properly conceived, they could form the basic structure of astronautical science. In this way, experts from each area could solidify his own ground thereby helping achieve the over-all goal of space flight.

One logical organization of these engineering sciences has been proposed by Darrell C. Romick. He emphasizes that the field of astronautical sciences is similar to that of the aeronautical sciences. Each is composed of a group of refined mechanical sciences that deal with vehicles operating in media not directly associated with the Earth's surface. Each involves three-dimensional motion, forces, inertia and equilibrium, and each is sensitive to the interplay of these quantities. Both fields are vitally concerned with the means for propelling and guiding the vehicles, and with the capabilities, limitations and well-being of the men who occupy and operate them.

Since aeronautics has undergone a natural evolution, it is best to use this field as a guide for astronautics. As an example, we can place aerodynamics next to *astrodynamics,* which is defined as that study dealing with the performance, stability and control of spacecraft. Similarly, the science of spacecraft propulsion would be similar to that of aircraft propulsion.

Astrodynamics represents a new science. It embraces everything that determines the behavior of a rocket vehicle that is guided and controlled by a specific system and propelled by a power plant of given performance characteristics. Just as with aerodynamics, the new science must look into the weight and balance of the rocket. In addition, it covers testing, corresponding to wind-tunnel and free-flight testing in aerodynamics. It includes an analysis of all regimes of spacecraft operation, such as aeroballistic (take-off within an atmosphere), powered ballistic (acceleration outside the atmosphere, or take-off from or landing on an airless body), unpowered ballistic (coasting trajectory of orbital flight), high-speed aerodynamics (atmospheric re-entry), airplane-type aerodynamics (glide and normal airplane-type landing approach), and special areas such as dynamic behavior during stage separation, trajectory corrections and emergency maneuvers.

Astrodynamics also will be called upon to make its contribution to the dynamic behavior of satellite stations. All these areas of dynamic behavior will have to be handled relative not only to the Earth but also to all sorts of planetary bodies, which means that various combinations of gravity, size and atmospheric characteristics must be studied.

Astrodynamicists will have an understanding of basic celestial mechanics, especially elementary orbital mechanics, including perturbations, precession, and other similar effects of planetary distortion or simple multiple-body situations.

Thus astrodynamics forms a fusion center, or hub, for integrating the efforts of the various other astronautical engineers and scientists. The astrodynamicist must generate spaceworthy vehicles with suitable performance, just as the aerodynamicist must bring together the efforts of the various other aeronautical engineers to provide air-worthy, high-performance aircraft.

Astronavigation is the second study proposed by Romick. This is essentially a wedding of the techniques and sciences of astronomy and navigation, bearing heavily on the principles of celestial mechanics. While the astrodynamicist uses some practices in this area, and works with the astronavigation engineer, it is the latter who carries full responsibility for knowing the effects of orbital mechanics on even the most detailed aspects of performance and maneuvering capabilities. He must also specify the equipment needed to meet any navigation operation.

Essentially, the work is that of devising and thoroughly studying the trajectories for various-type missions. Then this study must be converted to results useful to the astrodynamicist who must provide vehicle performance predictions. The other part of the job, specifying and providing navigational equipment, involves mostly the optical measuring equipment, backed up by suitable computing equipment. While the measuring equipment for determining direction and distance is mostly optical, the same objectives could call for radio direction and ranging equipment as well.

Spacecraft propulsion is the most obvious study. The field embraces all the propulsive devices that might be considered to get a vehicle into space, the characteristics and operation of the devices once they are in space, their performance, and all auxiliary equipment needed to keep the propulsive systems operating at design performance.

Spacecraft control system engineering calls for the design of systems needed to give stable behavior to the craft. The systems receive either human or mechanical guidance signals and actuate the devices that control the vehicle. These include gyros, autopilots, and servos. The engineers working in this field would be organized similarly to those doing corresponding work in the guided-missile field. Their work and many of the devices used would correspond. These engineers will work very closely with the astrodynamicist who will provide the operating criteria around which the control systems must be designed.

Spacecraft guidance engineering deals with systems that determine the path the vehicle is to follow. These systems include such items as preset programing devices, inertial guidance systems, radar devices and computers. This field is mostly restricted to vehicles operating between the Earth and a satellite station. Beyond this, it is mostly a job for astronavigation which uses settable programing devices. The guidance techniques used in the ascent to, and descent from, manned space stations will be similar to those used for missile guidance systems.

The responsibility of the *spacecraft structures engineer* is to provide for the integrity and efficiency of the vehicle structure. He must give the required strength at the lightest practicable weight. This is done by analyzing the stresses developed in the structure under the flight loadings determined by the astrodynamicist, and all other loadings applied to the vehicle. The work also involves a careful record and control of the weight, balance and moments of inertia of the structure and all other elements of the vehicle. In addition, he must do any necessary structural testing to prove his analysis and find basic data.

This work is analogous to the responsibilities and methods of the aircraft structural engineer, but an understanding of the basic principles of space vehicles is required. Skill and experience must be developed by those engaged in this work to apply properly this understanding to the structures involved. The unique character of the loadings on a vehicle in free space must be appreciated, and the structure must be made as light as possible to obtain the highest possible mass ratios, and corresponding vehicle performance.

Spacecraft design engineering will not differ much from the conventional design engineering performed by a competent aeronautical engineer. He will still have to use materials with high strength-weight ratios, materials that could be formed easily and cheaply, and probably materials that have better fatigue characteristics than those he has been using. He will have to consider the problem of *thermal fatigue* (loss of structural strength at high temperatures) much more than he is doing now, and will have to design his craft for a definite life span. The problem of large accelerations on the craft's structure will be met by increasing the loads on the structure, which is standard procedure. Some unique problems might arise such as the design of the shell of the vehicle in order to accomplish cooling of the skin when it passes at high speed through the atmosphere. But this problem has been anticipated and today is partly solved.

The *spacecraft equipment engineer* must provide not only the standard equipment adapted to the environment of a spacecraft but also the special equipment that will be needed. A few of these are the special windows, cabin air-purifying systems, processing and regulating equipment, fully adjustable and convertible acceleration chair-type seats, and equipment for operation during high accelerations. Visual indicating equipment will have to be readable during changing exterior lighting conditions without undue attention by the crew. Communication equipment such as headsets will have to remain in place and function under all conditions.

An interesting analysis of the factors that must be considered in the design of just two of the many instruments included in space-flight equipment has been given by ONR's Commander Hoover. He asks us to consider the knowing of time. Out in space will we have to consider local time, sidereal (star) time, orbital time, or elapsed time? We shall probably need all of them—local time for launching and return—sidereal time for position in the orbit—orbital time for the determination of perigee and apogee—and elapsed time for fuel consumption and the return flight. Another problem is that of determining velocity. Will we indicate knots, thousands of kilo-knots or per cent orbital speed? We have another difficult question. How will we measure velocity with self-contained units? These are only several of a mass of problems dealing with instruments alone.

The enormous need for all types of scientific talent in the coming spacecraft era is quite evident. The opening of the frontiers to space will bring investigators from practically every organized field. Beyond the call for engineers will be the cry for other personnel. Physicists will be asked to operate the laboratories in space. They will have to prescribe the instrumentation for the high-altitude studies of the ionosphere, cosmic rays, and magnetic fields. They will be needed to interpret the incoming data and prescribe further tests. On the basis of the new physical theories that will evolve, mathematicians will have to help formulate the concepts and solve the equations. For this, more versatile and accurate computers will have to be devised.

Chemists and biochemists too will operate their own space laboratories where the effects of altitude on chemical reactions and microorganisms will be investigated. Physical chemists will probably be sharing these laboratories to learn more about the construction of the atom and molecule. Meteorologists will be present to measure upper-atmospheric winds, gauge their turbulence, and learn the temperature gradients in the various atmospheric shells around the Earth. They will be striving to explain the mechanism of the auroras, of air glows, and of the sporadic magnetic storms occurring in the ionosphere.

Astronomers will service their observatories, unblocked by the atmosphere. From these they will be able to tell us someday the make-up of our planetary system, the true constituents of outer space, and perhaps even the construction of the Universe. The geophysicists will turn their sights on Earth. They will analyze the physical environment in which man has thrived so long. They will give us the size and shape of the Earth, and the value of the force that has bound us to it. We know that in the field of space medicine, or astromedicine, physicians will be studying the effects of weightlessness on the bodily functions. They also will be learning more about the effects of exposure to radiations unfelt on Earth.

The psychiatrists might be called upon to make up a new name for people suffering neuroses when left alone in space, and might have to devise means for entertaining people seeing nothing around them for long periods of time but vast volumes of blackness. The legal profession will be determining how far is up, and to whom it belongs. Many philosophers and sociologists will undoubtedly have to review some of their beliefs in the light of satellites that may barely be seen.

Many of the investigations we have outlined overlap other scientific disciplines. This is to be expected because science knows no boundaries, and from small areas it diffuses itself over the entire field of structured inquiry, and gives growth to new areas. So, too, the fruition and effects of conquering space will envelop much of science and human endeavor. First, we devise satellites and satelloids that orbit above the Earth's atmosphere. Next, we may design the ships that will take us to the Moon, Mars, and Venus. Later, like Columbus, we may speak of colonization.

REFERENCES

"Advance Man To The Moon", *Aero Digest*, October, 1951.

Alsop, J., and Alsop, A., "Project Big Brother", syndicated column, New York Herald Tribune, February 3, 1956.

Baker, N. L., "Engineering Problems Of Manned Space Flight", presented at an American Institute of Electrical Engineers meeting, Fort Wayne, Indiana, October 13, 1955.

Ballinger, E. R., "Human Experiments In Subgravity And Prolonged Acceleration", *Aviation Medicine*, August, 1952.

Beller, W. S., "Aero News Digest", *Aero Digest*, August, 1955.

Bergaust, E., "Foreign Missile Trends", *Aero Digest,* July, 1955.

Bergaust, E., "The Next Fifty Years Of Flight", Harper and Brothers, New York, 1954.

Berkner, L. V., "International Scientific Action: The International Geophysical Year 1957–58", *Science*, April 30, 1954.

Burgess, E., "Frontier To Space", The Macmillan Company, New York, 1955.

Canney, H. F., Jr., and Ordway, F. I., III, "The Uses Of Artificial Satellite Vehicles", presented at the Sixth International Astronautical Federation Congress, Copenhagen, Denmark, 1955.

Chapman, S., "Scientific Programme Of The International Geophysical Year 1957–58", *Nature*, March 5, 1955.

Clarke, A. C., "The Exploration Of Space", Temple Press Ltd., London, 1951.

Cummings, C. I., and Newberry, A. W., "Radio Telemetry", *Jet Propulsion*, May–June, 1953.

Duke, N., "Sound Barrier", Edward Lauchberry Philosophical Library, Inc., New York, June, 1954.

Ehricke, K. A., "Engineering Problems Of Manned Space Flight", *Interavia*, July, 1955.

Elvey, C. T., and Roach, F. E., "Aurora And Airglow", *Scientific American*, September, 1955.

Evans, J. W., "Solar Influence On The Earth", Annual Report of the

Smithsonian Institution, U. S. Government Printing Office, Washington, D.C., 1954.

Felt, N. E., Jr., "Development Of A Stabilization System For The Viking Rocket", presented at an American Rocket Society meeting, New York, November 30–December 3, 1954.

Gatland, K. W., Kunesch, A. M., and Dixon, A. E., "Minimum Satellite Vehicles", Proceedings of the Second International Congress on Astronautics, London, 1951.

Gautier, T. N., "The Ionosphere", *Scientific American*, September, 1955.

Glasstone, S., "Sourcebook On Atomic Energy", D. Van Nostrand Company, Inc., Princeton, New Jersey, 1950.

Haber, H., "Manned Flight At The Borders Of Space", *Jet Propulsion*, September–October, 1952.

Haber, H., "Can We Survive In Space?", in the book "Across The Space Frontier", Viking Press, 1953.

Haley, A. G., "Basic Concepts Of Space Law", presented at an American Rocket Society meeting, Chicago, November 14–18, 1955.

Haley, A. G., "International Cooperation In Rocketry And Astronautics", *Jet Propulsion*, November, 1955.

Haley, A. G., "International Cooperation In The Field Of Astronautics", presented at an American Astronautical Society meeting, New York, December, 1955.

Haviland, R. P., "On Application Of The Satellite Vehicle", presented at an American Rocket Society meeting, Chicago, November, 1955.

Henry, J. P., "A Report On Animal-Carrying Rockets", Aero Medical Laboratory, 1955.

Hoover, G. W., "Instrumentation For Space Vehicles", presented at an American Rocket Society meeting, New York, December, 1954.

Hoover, G. W., "Why An Earth Satellite?", presented at an Engineers Society of Milwaukee meeting, Milwaukee, Wisconsin, February, 1956.

Johansen, H. O., "Inside The New Midget Moon", *Popular Science*, January, 1956.

Kaplan, J., "Aspects Of The Earth Satellite Program", presented at an American Astronomical Society meeting, Troy, New York, November, 1955.

Kaplan, J., "Satellite And Rocket Exploration Of The Outer Atmosphere", presented at an American Rocket Society meeting, Chicago, November, 1955.

Kaplan, J., and Odishaw, H., "Satellite Program", *Science*, November 25, 1955.

Leonard, J. N., "Flight Into Space", Random House, New York, November, 1953.

Levitt, I. M., "Geodetic Significance Of A Minimum Satellite Vehicle", presented at the Fifth International Astronautical Federation Congress, Innsbruck, Austria, August, 1954.

Lindemann, F. A., "Conduction Of Electricity", Encyclopaedia Britannica, volume 8, 1945 edition.

Makowski, J., and Whitney, V. L., Jr., "Personnel And Equipment Cooling In Supersonic Airplanes", presented at an American Society of Mechanical Engineers meeting, New York, November 28–December 3, 1954.

Mannal, C., "Can Nuclear Energy Drive Interplanetary Rockets", *General Electric Review*, May, 1955.

Massey, H. S. W., "The Nature Of The Upper Atmosphere", Annual Report of the Smithsonian Institution, U. S. Government Printing Office, Washington, D.C., 1954.

Menzel, D. H., "Other Worlds Than Others", *Atlantic Magazine*, November, 1955.

Michael, D. N., "Man in Space: A Tool and Program for Research in the Social Sciences", unpublished proposal, Washington, D.C., November, 1955.

Newell, H. E., Jr., "High Altitude Rocket Research", Academic Press, Inc., New York, 1953.

Newell, H. E., Jr., and Siry, J. W., "Rocket Upper Air Research", *Jet Propulsion*, January–February, 1953.

Newell, H. E., Jr., "Scientific Uses Of An Artificial Earth Satellite", delivered at The American Museum-Hayden Planetarium, New York, August 16, 1955.

Newell, H. E., Jr., "The International Geophysical Year Earth Satellite Program", presented at an American Association for the Advancement of Science meeting, Atlanta, Georgia, December, 1955.

Newell, H. E., Jr., "The Role Of Rockets In The International Geophysical Year", presented at the Sixth International Astronautical Federation Congress, Copenhagen, Denmark, August, 1955.

Newell, H. E., Jr., "The Satellite Project", *Scientific American*, December, 1955.

Oberth, H., "Why The Race For The Moon?", *American Weekly*, October 2, 1955.

Olivier, C. P., "Aurora Polaris", Encyclopaedia Britannica, volume 2, 1945 edition.

"Out Into Space", *New York Times Weekly Review*, July 31, 1955.

Ovenden, N. W., "Meteor Hazards To Space-Stations", Proceedings of the Second International Congress on Astronautics, London, 1951.

Pendray, G. E., "The First Quarter Century Of The ARS", *Jet Propulsion,* November, 1955.

Petersen, N. V., "General Characteristics Of Satellite Vehicles", *Journal of Astronautics,* Summer, 1955.

Petersen, N. V., "Lifetimes Of Satellites From Near-Circular And Elliptic Orbits", presented at an American Rocket Society meeting, Chicago, November, 1955.

Prior, G. T., "Meteorite", Encyclopaedia Britannica, volume 15, 1945 edition.

"Proposed United States Program For The International Geophysical Year 1957–1958", U. S. National Committee for the IGY, National Academy of Sciences-National Research Council, Washington, D.C., August, 1955.

Raffone, J. J., "Acceleration Force And The Space Pilot", *Journal of Astronautics,* Fall, 1955.

Raisbeck, G., "The Solar Battery", *Scientific American,* December, 1955.

Rees, E., "Guided Missiles", *Time,* January 30, 1956.

Riblet, H. B., "Instrumentation Techniques and Requirements For Rocket and Guided-Missile Testing", presented at an American Rocket Society meeting, Baltimore, Maryland, April, 1955.

Romick, D. C., "A Suggested Organization Of Space Flight Sciences", presented at the Sixth International Astronautical Federation Congress, Copenhagen, Denmark, August, 1955.

Rosen, M. W., "Twenty Five Years Of Progress Towards Space Flight", *Jet Propulsion,* November, 1955.

Rosen, M. W., "The Viking Rocket Story", Harper and Brothers, New York, 1955.

"Round-Table Conference, Project Vanguard", *Aero Digest,* December, 1955.

Sänger, E., "Astronautics", *Aero Digest,* December, 1955.

Schachter, O., "Who Owns The Universe?" in the book, "Across The Space Frontier", Viking Press, 1953.

Schaefer, H. J., "Exposure Hazard From Cosmic Radiation At Extreme Altitude And In Free Space", *Jet Propulsion,* September–October, 1952.

Simons, D. C., and Parks, D. P., "Climatization Of Animal Capsules During Upper Stratosphere Balloon Flights", presented at an American Rocket Society meeting, Chicago, November 14–18, 1955.

Singer, S. F., "Design Criteria For Minimum Satellites", *Aero Digest,* April, 1956.

Singer, S. F., "Applications And Design Characteristics Of Minimum Satellites", presented at an American Rocket Society meeting, Chicago, November, 1955.

Singer, S. F., "Studies Of A Minimum Orbital Unmanned Satellite Of The Earth (Mouse)", presented at an American Rocket Society meeting, Baltimore, Maryland, April, 1955.

Singer, S. F., "The Mouse", delivered at The American Museum-Hayden Planetarium, New York, May 4, 1954.

Stehling, K. R., "Balloon Launching An Earth Satellite", *Aviation Age*, July, 1955.

Stehling, K. R., "Space Flight Notes", *Jet Propulsion*, September, 1955.

Stehling, K. R., "Space Flight Notes", *Jet Propulsion*, November, 1955.

Storey, L. R. O., "Whistlers", *Scientific American*, January, 1956.

Strughold, H., "Space Equivalent Conditions Within The Earth's Atmosphere; Physiological Aspects", *Astronautica Acta*, volume 1, 1954.

Strughold, H., "From Aviation Medicine To Space Medicine", *Aviation Medicine*, 1952.

Stuhlinger, E., "Electrical Propulsion System For Space Ships With Nuclear Power Source", presented at an American Astronautical Society meeting, New York, December, 1955.

Sutton, G. P., "Rocket Propulsion Elements", John Wiley & Sons, Inc., New York, 1949.

Tousey, R., "The Visibility Of An Earth Satellite", presented at the Sixth International Astronautical Federation Congress, Copenhagen, Denmark, August, 1955.

Townsend, J. W., Jr., "The Use Of Rocket Vehicles for Upper Atmospheric Research", presented at an American Rocket Society meeting, Baltimore, Maryland, April, 1955.

"Utility Of An Artificial Unmanned Earth Satellite", a proposal by the ARS Space Flight Committee to the National Science Foundation, New York, November 24, 1954.

Vaeth, J. G., "200 Miles Up", The Ronald Press Company, New York, second edition, 1955.

van de Hulst, H. C., "'Empty' Space", *Scientific American*, November, 1955.

von Braun, W., "Crossing The Last Frontier", *Colliers*, March 22, 1952.

von Braun, W., "Prelude To Space Travel", in the book "Across The Space Frontier", Viking Press, 1953.

von Braun, W., and Ryan, C., "The Baby Space Station", *Colliers*, June 27, 1953.

von Karman, T., "Guided Missiles In War And Peace", *Aero Digest*, July, 1955.

Waite, L. L., "Men Wanted For Missile Engineering", *Aero Digest*, July, 1955.

Wares, G. W., "Terminology And Nature Of Atmospheric Shells", *Jet Propulsion,* January–February, 1954.

"What Is The Viking?", Martin Company, Baltimore, Maryland, 1955.

Whipple, F. L., "Astronomy From The Space Station", delivered at The American Museum-Hayden Planetarium, New York, October 13, 1952.

Whipple, F. L., "Is There Life On Mars?", *Colliers,* April 30, 1954.

INDEX